The Tin Can House and Other Stories

THE TIN CAN HOUSE AND OTHER STORIES

Susan Pepper Robbins

Susan Pepper Robbins

for

Joanne & David

Charlottesville,

January 31, 2023

Attention schools and businesses: for discounted copies on
large orders, please contact the publisher directly.

"The Tin Can House" was previously published in *Verdad*
(Vol. 23, 2017)

For information contact:
Unsolicited Press
Portland, Oregon
www.unsolicitedpress.com
orders@unsolicitedpress.com
619-354-8005

Cover Design: Kathryn Gerhardt
Editor: S.R. Stewart

ISBN: 978-1-950730-57-5

TABLE OF CONTENTS

THE TIN CAN HOUSE

The A-Frame was shingled in flattened, tin oil cans on the wrong side, so the old names of Esso and Texaco didn't show. The sun shot a pale greenish light through the oak trees' April leaves. The tin house gave the right impression of one of the crazy projects thought up by our delicensed doctor, hammering out all those cans after using a can opener to take the round tops and bottoms off; those he used for decorative trim around the two doorways and four windows. Thousands of shingles nailed, one by one, three nails each, to the beams, in the 1950's. Some people continued to go to him not in his office, of course, which had to be closed, but to his ranch house where he would invite you in and listen to your symptoms. Not ours. We never went back to him after the sheriff picked him up for walking in the next county dressed as a woman. Who'd want to do that, Fred asked me, serious and not meaning anything about my beige and navy outfits.

Someone saw the rescue squad go down the road, and later we heard that the team had found Watson Booker stretched out by a log near the tin can house. In fact, at first, they had thought he was a log, he was so straight and brown, not curled up the way they thought a man would be from freezing. Watson was stretched out in the leaves, a light cover of snow and a few leaves blown up over him, his rifle propped up in the tin can house, where evidently he had been living when he wasn't walking the roads. He'd walk thirty miles, even more, every day, carrying the rifle. Sometimes people asked him to work, loading hay or wood, but there weren't any farms left in the county, just a few pulpwood lots, so there wasn't much heavy work, real farm work, to do anymore, only running the lottery machines at the gas stations or using riding lawnmowers to cut old people's yards. We live in a county with wireless, satellite dishes, SUVs, private academies, people who go on Australian cruises, and where a man can freeze to death.

That summer, when the river had sandbars, we predicted a brutal winter, and it is true that Lillian brought Tom home from Myrtle Beach in a wheelchair in December. They go to the beach in the winter because it's cheaper. There hadn't been anything wrong with Tom when they'd left home. We all said we'd get a wheelchair too, married to Lillian. Tom's no fool. But Tom and Lillian are another story.

After Watson Booker had been found, Fred said now we wouldn't have to worry about being shot by Watson. Fred and I were walkers for the breast cancer people, and we wore the pink ribbons on our insulated jackets. When Watson would pass us, he tipped his hat, as if it were a century ago, but his rifle was slung on his shoulder and we'd hear a shot after he got out of sight. "Rabbit," Fred would say.

We felt better after we joined the Cremation Society, the only club we were in. I didn't count the little country church as a club because Fred wouldn't go with me after Watson Booker had frozen to death less than two miles from the church, which was locked anyway. Fred asked what kind of club lets a man freeze outside its doors. He likes to try to make me see things his way. He grew up on a farm in the county and knows all the houses and their families, mostly dead. We have lived here since day one, our wedding day, when he broke down and cried like a baby. This humiliating scene I have never gotten beyond and will never forgive Fred for, but he often brings it up because he thinks he understands how some things, like *his* wedding, he calls it as if I weren't featured, do not lie too deep for tears and deserve tears. Some things should be wept over. The heart knows its reasons, he goes on. You can see, as I have said many times, why I love this man. This year he is reading Lacan and is struck by how we find our identities. Looking in the mirror, as babies love to do, is one way. I don't think so.

I was imported to this life in the deep piedmont, transported from northern Virginia to a suburb of

Washington, but I never adjusted to my life as an indentured servant, or immigrant, or an exchange student, Fred says. He does see me as a kind of exchange student here, but from an industrialized Bhutan, where people are happy for no good reason that we can see. It's been thirty years.

But it was a comfort knowing about the Society's twenty-four/seven service. I had seen with my own eyes, two men in nice gray suits come for Fred's aunt and take her out of the house with great care at three-thirty that morning last year, not bumping into the walls with the gurney, and going across the yard to their van, unmarked. Much better than the three-day ordeals we were used to when people died.

Fred's Uncle Clement, for instance, who had served a brief term in the state prison in Richmond for mail fraud, had, what was for us, a state funeral, and gave Fred's aunt—the one gently carried out of the house a year later—her best scenes of the heartbroken widow, her sons holding her up to walk into the church and to sit with her at the dinner that followed the long service. The minister had promised us all that we would be meeting Clement on the other side, where all the rough places were smooth. The sons, Clemmie Jr and David, inspired by the injustice they felt had been visited on their father for simply using the U.S. Postal

System, were both attorneys for white collar cases and had never lost in court.

Fred and I, at that point, did not want such a funeral for ourselves. Bea's had been enough. Poe is right to say that there is nothing more affecting than a young beautiful, dead woman. Something along those lines.

For one thing, our daughter Cynthia was through with us after Bea was killed and would never have shown up for such a "parade," she had said, knowing that I would like her use of Jane Austen's phrase. Even if I were sorry, she would not want to come to my funeral or her dad's, who was a much better dad than I was mom. Fred wants his ashes flying up from the car window as I drive on Route 6. That way he will escape at least some of the limits he lives with—he means speed limits, money limits, property lines, maybe his wept-over marriage vows, his darling daughter Bea's short life.

We both knew the story of Watson Booker. He had killed his brother, gone to prison for ten years for aggravated assault, and his family wouldn't let him come home, much less live there. "If the black community wouldn't take him in, we couldn't because it would cast a light on their judgment." Fred settled our white guilt. As I said, Fred knows many things. But we did pray for Watson during Joys and Concerns at church.

Fred had a harder time with the news that the postmaster, who had thick red hair, had been appointed and brought with him a wife who was thin and dark. Harder than with Watson Booker's freezing to death near the church. The new couple could have been in a fairytale. And yes, she ran away, though only a few miles, with a man thirteen years younger, a blonde mama's boy who had a high school sweetheart break his heart when she married a Richmond lawyer and drank herself to death. So that is why the blonde young man decided to go to law school, announced it to his mother who took a third job cleaning houses to put him through the University. He knew that the world would come to him, so he let the dark thin wife of the postmaster run a few miles up to his house, three miles, and nab him, Fred's word.

This is how Fred tells this story at one of our dinners. The postmaster found a much better wife nearby, a plump, also red-headed, but divorced, school teacher. They married and were happy. The young lawyer turned against his mother, who died in a Medicaid nursing home unvisited, because she would not sign the farm with the 1912 mansion on it over to him and the thin dark woman. So these two fairytalers began renovating Fred's great aunt's Victorian house with a wraparound porch, two or three gables, triangle windows, balconies, boxwood walks, iris borders, and wisteria vines clustered with pale lavender shaped blooms. He had some great old houses in his family. "Better than the people," Fred would add.

Fred did not do so well with the story of Becky and Paul, but he kept trying, and I did my part by coming up with different ways to use the venison we were given by the hunters who like to have tree stands on our one hundred twenty-three acres, what was left of the three hundred sixty Fred inherited.

Here is how Fred laid the story out on the table, so to speak. We all knew the story by heart and knew the phrases Fred would get to—funeral meats, the good furniture of the dead mother, and the not good things of Becky, the new person who was moving in with Paul. They knew that this Becky had been kicked out of her house, and so she had called Paul, her new boyfriend whose wife had died a little over a year ago, to come help her pack up. Paul had a truck, and he was doing exactly what she knew his friends, including Fred, and Paul's dead wife's friends, including me, were warning him about. A rescue.

It was true. Becky wanted to be rescued from her daughter, who was getting off her meds more and more and was impossible. Running out of the house naked, up and down the country road, no cars that time of night except the few people who drive in to make the biscuits at Hardee's. Even if it meant Becky would be leaving the eighteen-month-old granddaughter to somehow grow up with a crazy, road-running mother.

And there was the problem of Becky's husband. The divorce was not final. Becky needed help, and Paul was a helper. He had just finished seeing his Callie through her cancer to the end. Everyone knew Paul had been the best nurse in the world. Some things are what they are, even when we know they are headed in the wrong direction. Too soon, everyone was saying, too soon.

Becky knew and Paul knew about being unhappy and knowing what they knew made them feel above criticism and safe with each other. Paul had a big pretty house; Becky had nowhere to go. It was that simple, but Paul had children with children and ideas about who should live in their just-dead mother's big pretty house. They were afraid for their dad but could see he was trying to get a life, a new one. Paul's daughters, Janice and Helen, said the whole Becky thing—the dating and then the move—was too stupid, too sad for words, and made a comedy of Hamlet's joke about the funeral meat leftovers being used for the widow's wedding. So they refused to go help with Becky's move-in, which involved moving their mother's things out to a storage place and Becky's not-as-nice things in. The story repeated by Fred, the exact words repeated as the story went on was good to hear.

Janice and Helen were mothers of teens and were themselves Facebookers, texters, and online shoppers who knew that sixty was the new forty, but forty could be both stupid and dangerous. They were forty-two and forty-four and had made their own stupid mistakes, ones they'd rather not think about but were afraid Paul had already told Becky, chapter and verse.

It did not help to say to each other that it, meaning the whole mid-life crisis dating, was all stupider than stupid. That story we all knew. Well, maybe a little.

Fred invited Becky and Paul to dinner without telling me until that afternoon. He didn't forget; it was just that he felt free to invite them out of the blue, counting on me to make it all work. That's true love, he said in his infuriating, dark voice. It's southern hospitality, maybe Arab hospitality, to take in those who are lost in Virginia or in the desert. Fred, like me, had lived other places and had, like me, returned to his ancestral home(s), so he brought a new take to the old ways. What could I say?

That night—no venison, but what Fred said was chicken purlieu, almost as great as his mother's chicken purlieu, steaming on the table in the ironstone tureen from Charleston with the ironed thin napkins and

Lenox china, we swam toward helping Paul and Becky. How did we think we were qualified to help? Who will help the helpers? Nobody, is who.

Fred swam on, using his powerful Australian, swim team at the University stroke to tell the story of Sheila and Carl, the one with a dead person under a walnut tree—much more danger in each sentence and swallow of the cheap wine we served, than Becky and Paul could muster in their little story. They would feel better about their lives, their problems, after hearing about Sheila and Carl.

At the old library table in our dining room, ladling out, with his great aunt's silver spoon, the chicken purlieu, clearing his swimmer's throat, Fred began: "One evening, Sheila's husband found her letters to Carl."

Carl is my great nephew, so the story by all rights should have been mine to tell. Not a chance, but because Fred and I both had roots in the county he felt that my nephew was his nephew.

"So," Fred has picked up the modern way of beginning, "Sheila's husband, whose name is lost to history, put Carl's love letters to his Sheila on the dash of his truck and his loaded shotgun on the seat. Then he drove over to where Carl was staying, at Merle's, she's my wife's cousin and her house is thirteen miles from

10

us. When Merle came home that night and saw a strange truck parked in the wrong place in her yard, she was irritated. How would her grass stand a chance? But when she walked over to the truck, she almost stumbled over what looked like a large sleeping or wounded animal.

"Merle panicked, ran into her house, and called for help. Merle was in hysterics, but at that point the hysterics fell into a normal range for rural North America. She thought there was a bear or a deer out in her front yard by a stranger's truck. It might well have been a dead animal because her neighbor, in one of his alcoholic schemes, had draped a dead sheep over her fence, angry about Merle's complaints that his cows and sheep were getting out on the road. It never crossed her mind that it was a dead person, much less Sheila's husband. She'd never met Sheila or even heard of her, much less her husband. Merle is not the kind of person to ask questions. She had never asked Carl about where he had been when he did not come back to her house, which has an outside staircase to her attic where Carl had asked to stay when his wife, he said, beat him almost to death with the ironing board, which he did not know had so much metal in it."

We said later that it was a blessing Merle did not call the sheriff. We said that it was also a blessing that Carl had not been there in his attic room. Sheila's husband had had a heart attack, another blessing. No one was murdered. No one. Sheila and Carl had a nice wedding in the summer.

So, Fred let the obvious moral of the story hang over the supper party for Paul and Becky, the smears of the purlieu on the plates: Things work out. There does not have to be a shot fired. Paul seemed to get it, but Becky had questions, even though I felt that they were the wrong ones, like what kind of wedding it was and how much the caterer and florist cost.

DROWNING

The weekend of Irene's funeral, the Friday before the Saturday afternoon service for her, we heard that Martin Hillander had drowned. He had been fishing in one of the big ponds on Irene's farm, the twenty-acre one with a long dock and boat house. He and his friend Ron Booker had gone fishing early Friday morning to beat the August sun and had taken Ron's nephew who had a bad temper and had been sent home from Parris Island. The Marines couldn't deal with Gerald any more than his mother, Polly, could. Ron, we knew, had promised the judge to keep an eye on Gerald, and of course, Martin was a backup for his best friend Ron. Gerald was like Ron's baby brother, Polly's only child, and she had ruined him with motorcycles, cars, guns, boats—anything Gerald wanted.

Gerald was nineteen, a drop out, trouble from the get-go, everyone said. But Judge Simpkins knew what second, third, fourth and fifth chances meant to a young man, plus he had grown up with Ron and Martin. As a young man, before law school, before the judgeship, he had proposed to Polly, before she got herself in trouble with Gerald's dad, one of the no good

Lawsons. Then, he came to his senses and married Ginny, who had always loved him since third grade.

So, Gerald had been staying over with Martin and Liz, who took in refugees, even the illegals, because of the way they, both the Hillanders and the refugees, believed in more chances, and Liz and Martin thought that Gerald was a kind of illegal refugee.

What Gerald needed was someone to shoot him, not a sanctuary with a Liz Hillander, who was so gentle she had hummingbirds fly up to her face, nineteen, she claimed, and we believed her. She had them that tamed. At dusk they would flutter off to the woods. That's Liz for you, Martin would say as deep in love with her as when he first saw her. "I guess I am one of her hummers," he'd laugh. So what, we wondered, was Gerald, a wild cat who stalked birds.

Maybe Liz and Martin saw Gerald as taking a break from his mom, Polly, who was always after him to do something with his life. She would say, almost crying, "carpe diem," no longer adding, "seize the day," because she had been saying it to him all his life, especially in the mornings when he would not get up and go to school. His dad had run off, predictably, and Gerald understood why. His mom should have married the judge, as many people had let him know. Polly was a looker; he'd hear at the Food Lion when he could be bribed into picking up a few things. He'd do it for Liz and Martin quicker than for his mom, he couldn't exactly say why. He couldn't explain why he'd been sent home from Parris Island either, but it had something to do with sleeping in the cot next to a kid who was dead one morning. It was not only the dead guy but the whole stupid military thing, all the rules. Gerald knew he was a problem for his mom, the Polly everyone loved, and he knew he was a burden for Liz and Martin, partly because Martin was such a great guy, a SEAL for god's sake, and because they did not have children so had no idea what trouble was. He knew he was bringing them a boat load of trouble, but so far, they were holding up.

He'd heard Polly ask herself, sweetly of course, what people without children worried about, and maybe that's why he was staying in Liz and Martin's nice extra bedroom—to give them a taste of real life. His Uncle Ron couldn't take him in because, as everyone including the judge knew, Ron had a problem with alcohol. Who didn't? Gerald wanted to know, but being young, he didn't show it yet.

Ron always said, "my sister Polly is the only woman who can wear red lipstick." She was a looker, could have married anyone, but she turned them all down, as well as the future judge, to marry a man who drank, gambled, and fished—that was what he did for a living. They had Gerald and ruined him with indulgence and neglect.

Good judgment, or any at all, was not in Gerald's DNA from either side. Martin had thought the Marines would straighten Gerald out, but when he was sent home, Martin took him in to live with him and Liz, to get him away from his mother and his Uncle Ron, even a few miles. He was hoping that fishing with him and Ron, going to the races in Martinsville, riding the off-road trails, going bow hunting—anything that country life could offer—would make Gerald see what a good life he had. Martin and Liz made it all available to Gerald, and one of the perks in Martin's mind was the open invitation to go fishing in Irene's ponds. To Gerald, who had developed a taste for crime, this privilege was ashes, dust in his mouth, or as he told a friend, shit.

Martin Hillander's drowning in a farm pond, out in the early morning with friends? No one could believe it. Martin, the Navy SEAL, strong as a bull? He was sixty-one, raced motorcycles, dug his own fence posts, hunted every day of hunting season, walking through clear cut hills for sometimes twenty miles, and retired from the Richmond police. Not to mention his happy life with Liz.

Once when Gerald had shot a buck on a hunt with Martin, it swam across the river to the island and got hung up in the brambles. It was Martin who insisted that they were going to canoe across the high running river, not Gerald, to track down the wounded buck and kill it. Gerald had cursed the wounded deer and yelled to Martin that they should go home, it was almost dark. That was the time Martin saved Gerald's standing with the other hunters, by making Gerald get in the canoe and cross the river to find the wounded deer to kill. There was a standoff on the muddy bank, some grabbing and shoving. Ron saw it all and was ashamed of Gerald and never told Polly.

So when we heard that the boat with Martin, Ron, and Gerald in it had turned over, on a glassy pond in mid-August, where no one had to stand up to cast a line over the steaming surface because the fish practically asked to be caught and taken home for supper, it did not seem possible that it had been Martin who had drowned. No one, not a grown man, not Martin Hillander, of all people on earth, should drown in a pond.

It was inevitable, necessary, for us to make sense of the fact that a person could die in the river. The woman from Albemarle had died during the Flat Boat Festival week. She thought she could wade close to the bank where the thirty foot boat had nudged in, poled in, and gotten stuck in the sand, so she had walked into the bank from the boat, holding the side of the boat, called by the experts, a bateau, that used to bring salt, sugar and barrels of flour and china for Fred's grandmother from Richmond. This bateau festival-going woman thought she could do what she wanted to do in the heat of that June afternoon, cool off, wade into the river bank, why not? But she could not. The heavy boat made a little two-foot move, and pinned her to a rock just under the water so her chest, head, and arms were above water keeping her from drowning, but the boat kept nudging in, crushing her as the five strong men, there for the beer drinking and the women in their shorts and halters, ran down and tried in a hundred ways to push, pull, and even lift with a lever made out of a log, the boat out of the slow current and give her a few inches to be pulled clear, with her broken back and ribs. They could not do anything, so one of the women who had been on the poling crew down from Scottsville, sat in the water and held the dying woman's head, her arm under her head, to rest her neck while she died, talking to her. She had had Red Cross training but not for that.

That was in June, and now it was August when Martin Hillander drowned the day before Irene was buried with all the ceremony we could muster on that Saturday. It should have been Gerald, not Martin, if anyone drowned. Gerald was the one who should have died in the river, not the Albemarle woman who, we heard, had never had a drink and had been a first timer on the bateau crew. A Southern Baptist.

Irene always said that bad people don't die young or suddenly, in accidents. They stick around to make other people take care of them. She was the only person we knew who said that she looked forward to being in the nursing home with all the people looking after her. When Polly heard that Martin was dead, drowned, they had to get the doctor to give Polly, not Liz, shots to calm her down enough, to stop her from throwing herself off the dock at the pond. Liz stopped her, telling her it would not help Martin. It was too late. Everything was. Polly must have known at some level that Gerald had his hand in Martin's drowning.

The only other person who had drowned in that pond was a four-year-old girl who had wandered down from her back door to that pond in the field. She had gotten under the fence and wanted to try the bathtub boat she had been given for her birthday.

There was no autopsy ordered for Martin, but we heard that Ron had said when he dove off the boat to try to get Martin that his arms had been locked up tight as a drum, which suggested somehow a heart attack had pitched him over the side of the boat and straight down to the bottom of the pond, twenty-six feet deep at that point. As far as we knew, Gerald did not dive in to help Martin.

Drowning was drowning, even caused by a heart attack, shameful for any man. We were all caught up that week in Irene's death, which was "louder" than Martin's drowning. Hers was operatic, more prepared for, more in tune with the way her life had been. She had stormed out of the hospital eight days before she died, refusing any help, and had driven home, furious with the nurses who had followed her out to the parking lot asking if there was anyone they could call to come get her, telling her that she had a detached retina and blood pressure of one eighty.

"I am going to hell, and can't wait to get there," she had yelled, and drove herself home, fifty-three miles, weaving and running the few lights before she hit the interstate. We heard about the scene in the hospital parking lot from Zoe who had gone to the hospital after the funeral to find out what had happened there with her mother. But it was Aster who remembered the tombstone in the barn that Irene had ordered for herself years before.

Polly had known about the tombstone and thought that it offered Irene some relief, some sense that she had done some good. Polly wished that she could carve something that suggested a good deed in her own life on a tombstone, especially that she'd been a good mother, but she knew that would make anyone who'd known her and her son smile.

Now her brother's best friend Martin, who had stepped up to take in Gerald, had drowned, and worse to think about was that Gerald had been there in the boat with his Uncle Ron who had done so much for him and with Martin who had done even more, while she sat at home waiting to hear more bad news which never failed.

At Irene's funeral, her husband, Dab, was the last one to speak as we stood in the blazing afternoon, the portable keyboard piano balanced against a tree in the old cemetery with the pianist from church banging out the hymns about crashing waves and saints, Irene's white hunter jumper saddled with one stirrup thrown back across, as if we were watching Kennedy's funeral, a hundred of us standing around the grave.

Dab said that he knew that many of us had felt Irene's anger, but there were more of us, including him and their daughters, Zoe and Aster, who had known her sweetness. He went on about a cracked surface on a porcelain cup that held a sweet, strong coffee for us to drink. It was such a great, such a gracious thing to say as we brushed away the mosquitoes, that we went along with it, thinking that if Dab, some of his bruises from Irene yellowing under his seersucker suit, could say these good things, then we could too, at least for the funeral. Aster was crying her eyes out.

Then we went back to Irene and Dab's house, the eighteenth century four room house, enlarged every fifty years until it was a long twisting house in a field with one huge pecan tree by the drive. No one that afternoon mentioned the news that Martin Hillander had drowned the day before with his friend and his nephew right there in the boat with him. We had enough on our plates. Polly, Ron, and Gerald did not come to Irene's funeral because they had to get ready for Martin's. Liz did not come, of course.

Three months earlier, I had stopped by Irene's for a visit. She had called me at six-thirty that morning to say I never visited her, and when I said had been with her all afternoon two days before and washed and curled her hair, she said that I always was correcting her. That afternoon there was another visitor, not unusual for there to be several people in Irene's bedroom that had chairs in a semicircle at the foot of the bed tricked out in a canopy, and with dishes from a few meals not quite hidden in the covers. This woman introduced herself as Mary Kinkaid. My heart jumped and I blurted out, "My daddy ran over your brother, or maybe it was you when you were little."

She looked at me as if she had heard, "Nice weather today," and said, "No, it was Robert, and he's fine."

It was years later from the night when daddy had confessed—that has to be the word—that he had backed over a child in the driveway, in the dark and yes, he'd had a few drinks. I said to this Mary Kinkaid, a retired math teacher, that I would send Robert a pie. Mary smiled as if I had said, "It's beginning to rain."

It had not rained for six weeks. The river was low, warm and black, the fields were brown, only the pine trees were green, and the yellow swallowtails dipped in and out of the planted rows of pines where blackberry bushes grew in furious defiance of the drought.

J.T. wrecked his boat on a rock—the river was so low—when he and Tina took his dad and mom out fishing on Sunday afternoon. It broke the old man's leg in two places and J.T. had to carry him up the boat landing, J.T. with his blood pressure problem. But, thank god, he could still drive the boat after it had hit the rock, and somehow he got them back to the landing where he slung his two-hundred-fifteen-pound dad over his shoulder and carried him to his truck. His mom and Tina were able to walk behind them, holding the old man's head to keep it from bobbing against J.T. The boat was declared totaled and the insurance gave him a new boat, but his dad was in the hospital for two weeks. J.T. kept saying, "My dad did not need that. Not mama either. They just wanted to go fishing on Sunday afternoon so Tina and I took them. We sure did."

He called the rescue people when he got his dad in the truck and they met him at Zion's Crossroads. Tina's leg was bruised, but they did not think it was that bad until a month later, she found out she had bone cancer. Six weeks later, Tina was dead.

A year later, when I told J.T. that I was sorry for all the sadness he had, he smiled and said he should have drowned his old man's "sorry ass." I wished that Dab had been there to talk about cracked cups still holding coffee, but of course, he was dead.

Fred and I did not know how to think of these accidents—if Martin's death were an accident—like the nice woman's from Albemarle when she was crushed by the bateau, and like the four year old wandering away from the back door to the pond, and like J.T's taking his mom and dad out on the river that was too low, hitting a rock, and setting off the cancer in Tina. We tried to think ACCIDENTS, but we couldn't.

TWO HUSBANDS

I married my first husband for all the wrong reasons which I won't go into but will summarize by saying they all could be categorized under Desperate Vanity. I still do not know what else to name it, a blankness about the future that needed me to fill with some action, so I did, and lived to regret it. I am sure he has too. He was a friend, in my class all through elementary school and high school, the valedictorian, in fact. He went to the University and failed out of the school of architecture for which he had some talent, and then transferred to the school of commerce where he did fine. His roommate was very wealthy but deeply depressed by the burdens of wealth, burdens that seemed like ones from fairy tales—the sad mother of the prince, the troubled king, and the bags of gold.

Add to the list of bad reasons, this first husband was the exact opposite of my father—sober, self-righteous, self-interested, ambitious. What he saw in me was a wife.

And, add to my reasons for marrying the first husband, my stupid sympathy for the catastrophes in his life: his crazy mother in and out of the hospital, and his own fall out of an old mill on the farm, the moated grange that crushed his face and shattered his legs and arms, though the doctors said it was a good thing he had fallen like a cat on all fours, even though his face took the hit. If he had fallen backwards, he would have cracked his head open.

So there was that element of the rescue and my boundless sympathy; I would marry the broken man, just as mama had married the alcoholic. It is all very clear to me. But not then.

Later there was Fred, the second husband, who asked me after six months to stop introducing him that way. "Florence, do you know how it sounds to other people? I don't mind, myself because I am glad to be your husband in any lineup." Yes, I could, so I ceased and desisted.

POTATO SALAD

The day I got fired I had made potato salad and my French bread for the faculty luncheon, knowing that I'd get the usual compliments for the bread. No one made bread, and even though very few of the women ate bread, they felt that they should when I announced that I had made it that morning. It all went because of the men who would eat anything, the women said, not meaning it the way I took it.

At the end of the lunch, there was enough potato salad left in the big green bowl shaped like a wilted cabbage leaf for another meeting. So, I felt pretty good at that point. Another semester starting. Even though, even though.

My husband's (the second husband, Fred) doctor had said we both should avoid using "but" in sentences, as in, "I meant to tell you, but . . ." or, "It was early, but . . ." The doctor had not condemned "even though," so I had at it with those two words. And, in private, inside my head, I relied on "but" to make sense of things: I'm married again, but . . . or, he seems happy, but . . .

It was after the lunch when we had all gone back to our offices to get ready for the next week when classes started that my department chair, Dr. Palmeri, had come clicking down the hall. Not unusual, not at all. She admired my friend, who had invited me to share her office eight years ago and, in fact, had gotten me the job at the downtown community college where I had seen everything in my classroom from a desk thrown—not at me—to an epileptic seizure and the water breaking as a young woman, very smart, took her exam, did not panic, and then let herself be taken to the hospital to have her baby.

Felice, my office mate, who became a real friend, had lived in Paris after college for two years and seemed Parisian. Gamin bangs, fast walk, hip jutting out when she answered a question. All French to me. In fact, the story got out that Felice had grown up in Paris and was really a French citizen, which was nice until it wasn't after the invasion of Iraq that France objected to and then the students wouldn't eat French Fries in the cafeteria for about two weeks. Then the story about Felice went that maybe she had a dual citizenship because she had a Tidewater, Virginia accent. But Felice really was American as she would say laughing whenever she was asked. But she did love Paris and went every other year. She got to use "but" with impunity as Montresor says about killing his friend Fortunato.

Felice had bought books in Paris from George Whitman and his daughter at their bookstore and knew that he claimed to be Walt Whitman's great-something. She knew the editions of *A Moveable Feast* and what the revisions did to change the account. Her mother had taught in Paris for years, not English but Greek and Latin, and when she retired to Richmond, she always took her Horace volume to read on the bus, not the Loeb with the side-by-side translation, the one I had used in college when I had trouble with the odes.

It was clear to me, painful, that Dr. Palmeri was puzzled that Felice could be so close to a person as plain, as un-French as me. Me, who had never been to Paris, and would, it now seemed with my out-of-work husband and young children, never go. But I have camped across America, I would say defensively, with my first husband, hoping to add interest to my resume. That ended that. What was nearly drowning in an Illinois campground compared to living for several years in Paris?

Dr. Palmeri, the Baby Dolphin, as I called her behind her back and it caught on, had tried to befriend me too, but it was slightly insulting to be liked simply because Felice liked me.

Maybe friendships worked this way—spider webbing out to others. Still, crumbs do make a feast. The Baby D. had tattoos up and down her arms, faded, but there, and she wore short sleeved tops as if her arms were beautiful, a sense of self which I admired.

What Felice and I had in common was what some would say was all that mattered—our drunk fathers and our childhoods drenched in secondary drunkenness, waiting on Christmas Eve for the tree to be dragged through the front door, and left just inside the door, with a slurred, "There, I found one." Both sets of our parents had made a move to the country in the late 1940s, returning to the simplicities of rural life, Felice's grandfather an Edinburg-trained doctor, my own a rural mail carrier who had to row across the James River to pick up the canvas bags of mail and then deliver them from a horse and buggy and later a Model A. But he had a blue-blooded name, last names from his grandmothers, so he had the manners of Felice's doctor grandfather.

Clicking down the ivory colored tiled hall to Felice's and my office where plants filled the ledges and gave the sky out of the third floor windows a fringe of green, Baby Dolphin handed me a thick sealed envelope, looking stricken, tottery in her pumps, and in retrospect, her tattoos seem to glow a little against her pink arms. She would not stay, even when Felice asked her to—not knowing what was in the letter.

I open the letter, thinking it must be a big committee assignment, one maybe funded by a federal grant that required a special contractual agreement with a faculty member.

I am preparing my demurral that would lead up to my refusal to serve on such a project because of the night meetings with faculty from other colleges, my long drive home where Fred and I have moored ourselves in his great aunt's old house, the trips to conferences, and the long reports and studies. This envelope should go to Felice. I am the wrong person, and I am ready to offer thanks for the confidence shown in my as-of-yet untested committee life even after eight years. Untested because of my clever footwork, avoidance of all extra classroom work.

It is a letter of termination after eight years on the faculty. So, the snake at my window last week, an upstairs window, had meant something. "But it's just a black snake," Fred had said, holding the flashlight on the lifted and waving head inches away from the screen.

"Just" should be another bad word, I had yelled at him, which made him smile.

It's just a letter, I said to Felice, and asked her to help me spoon up the leftover potato salad into the little containers I had learned to carry with me whenever I took food to a party or meeting. Someone always took it home.

STUPIDITY

Another distraction from ourselves, moored, swamped, or, as Fred called us, "painted ships upon a painted ocean," trapped in our grief for Bea, and from Watson Booker's frozen corpse by the tin can house, comes again from Merle on one of her very early morning visits. She comes for coffee between five and six. Any later got into the day, wounded it, she said.

We knew the story about Paul and Becky, but we liked to hear it again and again to see if we really got what it meant: when Becky Dunham had to move out, was driven out, she had called Paul, her new boyfriend whose wife had died a little over a year ago, to come help her pack up. He had a truck. He was doing what Merle and Paul's dead wife's friends had been warning him about. A rescue.

It was true. Becky wanted to be rescued from her daughter who was getting off her meds more and more and was impossible to live with. Even if moving out meant Becky would be leaving the eighteen-month-old granddaughter to somehow grow up with a crazy mother. Fred and I envied Becky her set of problems. Try having a dead daughter, we always thought at this point when we re-heard about Paul and Becky. At least there was a living baby. There was hope. That flimsy thing with feathers, Fred said later.

And there was, we knew, the problem of Becky's husband. The divorce was not final. Becky needed help, and Paul was a helper. He had just finished seeing his wife through her cancer to the end. Everyone knew Paul had been the best nurse in the world. I could feel Fred thinking at this point that I would not be a bad nurse and that we could avoid Home Help or hospice.

Some things are what they are, even when we know they are headed in the wrong direction, can see them veering off toward the cliffs. Too soon, everyone was saying to Paul, too soon.

Merle explained that both Becky and Paul knew a great deal, maybe everything, about what could go wrong, and knowing what they thought they knew made them feel safe with each other. And, Paul had a wife-less, a de-wifed—Merle's word—big pretty house: Becky had nowhere to go. It was that simple. We liked this part of the story, the boiled down part, the part we knew by heart.

Only, it was not simple at all. Paul had children with children and ideas about who should live in their just dead mother's big pretty house. They were afraid for their dad but could see he was trying to get a life, a new one. Paul's daughters, Janice and Helen, said the whole Becky thing—the dating and then the move—was too stupid, too sad for words, and they joked for the forty-eleventh time, as Uncle Clement said, about the funeral meat leftovers at the Elsinore wedding. Paul's daughters refused to help in any way with Becky's move-in, or invasion as they said, except to move their mother's silver and Windsor chairs out to a storage place and Becky's silver plate and department store furniture in.

Janice and Helen were mothers of teens and were themselves Facebookers, texters, and online shoppers who knew that chronological age did not mean what it used to—sixty was the new forty, and forty could be, and was in their dad's case, teenagerish, stupid, and dangerous. They themselves were forty-two and forty-four and had made their own stupid mistakes, ones they'd rather not think about but were afraid Paul had already told Becky about their "issues."

It did not help us to say as we always did about this story to each other early in the morning—Merle, Fred, and I—that it was all stupider than stupid. Well, maybe a little.

CICERO WAS WRONG

I am sorry to say that Cicero was wrong—if it was, in fact, Cicero who said it—that not to know history meant that you were going to repeat it. Hell or high water. Every day I see people who know their histories very well going forward busily repeating them. Melissa married a man just like her father, a bully. Pete married a woman just like his mother, a hysteric who felt hated by everyone except those who did not know her very well.

In my own case, knowing my own history made me repeat it, but in an opposite way, and in a way I could not see was an inexact replica, a mirror image of the past. Fred wasn't an alcoholic like daddy. In fact, a drink, even vodka, made Fred sick and embarrassed him. What kind of man can't take a drink, he'd say. But he was as dysfunctional as daddy, a better word for a husband than suicidal. Knowing our own histories condemns us to repeating them either verbatim or in an opposite way.

DESPERATE MEASURES

The river had sandbars that summer when Lillian brought Tom home from Myrtle Beach in a wheel chair. There hadn't been anything wrong with him when they left for a week at the beach as if they were an old married couple, and not just a dating adulterous pair. Fred said he'd get a wheel chair too. He's no fool. When he visited Tom, all Tom could say was that lilies were blooming their heads off and that we could all take comfort in that fact. It was like Tom to talk at an angle to facts.

Even the azaleas were dying in the drought, even the day lilies that Tom saw blooming in asphalt cracks. Those of us who knew Lillian said Fred was right and we'd get wheelchairs too if we had to live with Lillian. It was as brilliant a move as any that Tom had made over the years. Very impressive. He loved Lillian, not just for her money, but for her land, and her love of both, but especially her love of rolling hills, timber stands, low grounds that flooded when we used to have floods. Lillian had inherited fifteen hundred acres which was many more than the thirty that Tom's family had. My brother Ed, Tom's lawyer, told Tom that he himself would go down to the wire to keep his hand in with

Lillian—those acres. This was when Tom had gone to Ed to ask him to start divorce papers for him and Charlotte, before he moved in with Lillian. Tom was on the verge of suicide—he could live in the wheelchair with Lillian, but first, he had to get rid of Charlotte, his high school sweetheart, or one of them. He'd had to marry her, I mean, nothing could have stopped him. It wasn't that she was pregnant. Not Charlotte, not until she wanted to be, and she would have girls when she did have children. She would say she'd put a baby boy up for adoption.

Who can explain love? Not the poets, not the shrinks. The only true line about love that I know is one from a poet, but I am limited as my grandmother always told me, kindly, but often. It's true, so true, as that poet told us—we want to be loved for ourselves alone. Tom did not understand that he had not loved Charlotte for herself alone and he was repeating history with Lillian—her land, not herself was it. So the wheelchair was fine with him. Amazing to watch.

"You're a fool," Ed told Tom, but drew up the divorce papers. Ed got Tom a room in Appomattox and tried to make jokes about armies and defeat. Charlotte somehow knew where Tom would go, and she went after him, not with a gun, but with the deed to the land, as persuasive as a gun, the one Tom used to bring squirrels home for the stews he made.

Who'd have thought that church-going Charlotte would go after Tom and turn over her land to get him to come home? She got to the motel, but Tom was not there to take what she was offering. Lillian must have thought that she had Tom, hooked, lined, and sunk in the wheelchair. Plus, she had land, not as many acres as Charlotte, but cultivated pasture land for the Black Angus herd that Tom saw as his. So he gave up the land Charlotte had and took what Lillian had on offer.

FIRED

There must have been thousands standing in the rain that day. It was a late May graduation, and later we knew that it was only 1,643 who attended, but because we were all damp, and huddled together, it felt like a huge crowd. The rain was warm, but the air was not, a strange thing, maybe the climate changing, which many of the parents thought was part of an agenda to make us forget the threat of terrorism.

I had organized moving the graduation from the lawn in front of the college library to the gym, helping the Buildings and Grounds people with the signs, the tarp over the entrance and the extra chairs. I had been there since five that morning as the skies got lower and lower until I persuaded President Wilcox to say we should go ahead with setting up in the gym.

The day after graduation, I was fired. This was my second firing. I had been there for almost twenty years—running the place—a small college—but from the back seat. I was the dean's secretary, and part time teacher, filling in for anyone in the English Department for short terms, not a full-time assignment because that would have brought down the hounds of accreditation on us, and Fred had been assistant comptroller for the same number of years. I was a hybrid, degrees in Victorian novels and business so I knew the culture, I'll call it, of a decanal office. Things changed when Fred got promoted suddenly, overnight. The comptroller, his boss, dropped dead on the golf course, the one that he had persuaded the college to buy as an investment to save the endowment. After the funeral, we went out and bought our dream house, the one that became a nightmare, one of the houses in Fred's family, out in the country where he'd grown up and a few miles from me, where my cousin Merle had bought a fixer-upper rancher, to be flipped, she said, laughing, knowing she would never flip it, and was there for the duration.

We thought we needed a house with an attached apartment for one of our daughters—we weren't sure which one it'd be. At that point, we had two daughters and did not know how lucky we were. Both had problems, too many to go into. Let's just say Cynthia needed to be with us, but she hated the thought and sometimes us. We had done something wrong, but we were not sure what. At that point, Bea was living her life, "living large," she'd say, in law school. She'd be dead the next year.

Cynthia said once that we took up all the room with our grief for Bea and left her high and dry. We don't mean to, I'd yell. Motive does not matter, she said. It's action, not talk. We talked about Bea all the time, Cynthia said, as if Bea were still around. In a way, I'd say, she is. Yes, because of you, Cynthia said. Let her go, Cynthia said, talking to me as if I were a pharaoh who was holding Bea in bondage. "Let her be dead," she'd add bitterly sometimes.

At twenty-five, Cynthia could pass for a freshman, so her situation was hidden. She looked like a young person who was still in school.

She had freshman hair, jeans, hooded eyes, drug connections, had been on academic probation most of her college years, but not suspended or expelled, and miraculously had graduated with, of all things, a degree in psychology. She knew she was not expelled because of us, a fact that made her madder at us.

The day I was fired—as I say, my second RIF (reduction-in-force)—the dean called me into his office, asked me to sit down, and fixed me a cup of his green tea which I had been pretending I liked for the three years he'd been the dean, only I had been the one who fixed it for him but had to have a cup too so I wouldn't make him feel that he was using me in unprofessional ways. Taking the cup, I felt I was in a modern nightmare version of a Henry James scene where social gestures are pinpricks of betrayal stabbing like knives. So, I was bleeding profusely before the conversation ended, the green tea drunk.

Dean Caldwell said that he hoped what he had to tell me would not ruin our friendship or damage the way I felt about President Wilcox, who had complimented me on the way I handled the graduation move to the gym. That word, friendship, struck me like a thrown book, but only glancing, just grazing my shoulder because I still did not get it. I was being asked to resign, he then said, as if he were saying that I was being asked to take on another project, like the assessment reports that were due in the accrediting association office, ones which I had already been working on, knowing that I was the one to get them ready for him to sign. I knew how to present the efforts (none) the college had made to address the issues the last visit from the accreditors had exposed and the college had promised to "take steps toward resolving." Students were failing out, being arrested for various things including assault and worst of all, students were not applying to the college in the first place. Death was in the air, but I knew how to explain it as renewal and a period of introspection, with new committees appointed.

I laughed, bruised only slightly on my left shoulder, not a wrinkle in my summer linen blouse, my pearls hanging calmly—Fred's mother's cultured pearls. I said the thought of resigning had never crossed my mind. We'd bought the house near the home Fred's great aunt had grown up in. When Fred got the promotion to comptroller, well, as the interim, we had made our move to the old house, not seeing this trap that was being set by the college to get rid of me or Fred. Conflict of interest, somehow. Or, maybe it was not a trap, or maybe it was the oldest trap, quicksand, indifference, and convenient pragmatism. Attrition encouraged. Get the lesser one of us to resign, me, or if they were lucky, Fred and I would both walk away, insulted and free.

That's how Fred got promoted, and the Board of Visitors pointed to a conflict of interest, a condition that would, Dean Caldwell said, compromise the college's standing for accreditation. One of us must leave. He hoped I understood what was at stake for the college. It'd have to be Fred or me.

I, who knew so many of the compromises and had hidden them in the language of the reports I wrote for the administration, had to cough. Here, Dean C. as the students call him, some with filthy intent, ripped out a tissue for me from the box he had on his desk, one hidden in a leather box. I dutifully wiped my (dry) eyes. I did not have to leave–leave, just step away, fill in at the library for the person who was taking a semester off for health reasons.

In my new temporary job at the circulation desk, I started wearing tops with glitter on them, no more linen and pearls. As the fill-in for the woman who is on oxygen but still smoking at home thinking her job is waiting for her, I am lit up in my new tops, thinking there is hope that I will get her job.

I did not answer Dean C. but just kept drinking the green tea, using the tissue to cough some more, and then asked for a second cup, forcing him to go on and say that if I did not resign, the college would have to terminate me, but it was in my best interest to make the decision, to see my way to new opportunities. There were benefits to a resignation that were not available to a termination. Did I understand? And, if I resigned I could have the fill-in position at the library.

Not a question, because he knew that I was beginning to. I did not say that our new mortgage was close to three thousand a month, that the bills from Cynthia's last court appearance for her second DUI were twice that, and that Bea's funeral was not paid for. I was scheduled for surgery on my carpel tunnel wrists—not covered in the college's insurance plan.

I thanked him and asked if I could think about it overnight and he said no, that my decision was needed that afternoon. The Board of Visitors was on campus and this issue would come up.

When had ever such a minor matter as this one been on the docket at a Board meeting I wanted to ask, but did not want to go there, as Cynthia loves to say. I prepared all the agenda for those meetings and knew this was a first.

It came down to this: Fred would lose being the head honcho, interim at this point, of the monies, or I would lose my job. One of us had to go. Fred was, for the two weeks he'd been the interim after the funeral of the golfer, set to make three maybe four times what I did, so it was a no brainer, but still.

In the end, of course, I resigned, there was a party and a gift, and in two weeks, I was filling in at the library for the woman on oxygen.

My glittery tops and my highlighted hair give me a fierce and unsettling, yes, frightening force when students walk up to the desk. There are not many of them because they all do things online. Skim the assignments.

Merle avoids saying I look cheap. She is a kind person and knows that I am trying not to be myself. But she notices the effort to change, as does Fred who calls it bravura—the lipsticks and nail polish. He thinks we are smart to have the attached apartment ready for Cynthia, who as a four-year-old wore tiaras and tulle to school not just to her dance recitals. Fred says that we are doing what we can, meaning that with one dead daughter already, we must not have another one. Merle takes it all in and nods.

GRIEF

This is the phone call from Louise Holcomb. Merle kept it on her phone and played it for Fred and me. We thought it was an effort to say to us that we weren't the only ones with a dead child. There were many others who knew this terrible fact of life. Maybe we should count our blessings, recognize what had happened and that life, such as it is, goes on, and that we were getting too bent out of shape to go on. Louise's voice on Merle's phone was distilled and, as matter of fact, as expensive bourbon. She told Merle, who had not been on duty as a dispatcher for the rescue squad, what had happened to Arthur. Louise told Merle about finding her dead son.

"When I got to Arthur he was sitting up just as perfect as could be, not a mark on him, not a drop of blood, but when I lifted up his hand, I had to hold the dead weight of it, and I knew right then. He was gone. Of course, he had been drinking, but Ronnie was dead drunk, but not dead, lying passed out beside the big pine tree he had driven into at over a hundred, the trooper told me. I got there before the rescue squad—you weren't on duty, Merle, I am sorry to say, or I believe that Arthur would have gotten to the hospital quicker—so I was able to tell the squad where to look for Ronnie after they could see that my Arthur was gone. Ronnie, who is still alive, and the Lord knows he shouldn't be, is the one who got Arthur started on all the pills and other things. Ronnie was about fifty yards away from the car that was tore up completely, still breathing. No surprise. Too mean to die. Let others die. The radiator was pushed all the way through the engine to where Arthur was sitting, but it stopped short just before it hit him and messed him up. At least I could stand to look at him and touch his face."

Fred and I could see what Merle meant for us to understand about other people having terrible things to bear, to live through, finding a dead child. We had been spared what Louise Holcomb had gone through. We are not the only ones with broken hearts or ones that are breaking but could be, maybe, repaired. Miracles happen.

Merle had brought Louise Holcomb's phone message to us as a gift, as medicine, and, to our credit, we are trying. Grief feeds egotism, I think. Survival instincts will set in, but at first, they lag behind, stuck in place.

LOVE TESTS

In the afternoon, the men built a catapult, using four trees they had cut down that morning, lopping off the branches with axes—no chainsaws allowed. Then, they drove three cars fifty miles to the Home Depot in Richmond for the six hundred pounds of concrete it would take to set the logs in the holes they had dug with pickaxes and shovels in the backyard of the 1911 half-renovated house. They could have been working on the floors, hanging the doors, anything that would have made the house a place someone half decent would want to rent, maybe with a family. It had five bathrooms, five bedrooms, a huge kitchen with granite counters and two stoves, two sinks, everything. But now the house stood empty without doors for the bedrooms or bathrooms and with only the subflooring. A spotlight that automatically came on at dusk was keeping the vandals away, the same ones that had wrecked it before it was half-renovated and the spotlight was set up.

There were eight men, Fred's cousins plus some friends, all either engineers or headed that way, all bible literalists, all in love with wars and rumors of wars. That phrase hung in my head because the bright, sunny

Jehovah's Witness had visited me that same afternoon and read the frightening passage from Matthew, then we had prayed in my living room seven miles from Fred's grandmother's place where the medieval construction was going forward, in slow motion, by his young cousins.

Two of the cousins stayed with us, the others camped out and made fun of Eric and Mark who chose our beds and running water and my cooking to their fish fried on a Coleman stove, our electricity and flushing toilets to their flashlights and compost toilets behind the trees. Both groups had battery run video games. We had taken away the television from our daughters and had just recently gotten it back for us, for the PBS specials and the news. It was growing on us and we felt guilty for making our daughters more unhappy than they already were, Bea, not having a year left to live, feeling unlucky to have such drips, such doofuses, such hippies for parents. We weren't exactly those types, but whatever, as they'd say, or as Mercutio says about his wound, it'd "do."

I was the worst thing a mother could be for daughters—an English teacher, but not a full-time one with tenure and its perks, really a full-time secretary/library assistant/fill-in teacher for professors on sabbaticals or sick, and then demoted to a substitute circulation desk person.

I have heard Fred laugh many times that he hated grammar, the gerunds the most and participles the next most. I was beginning to see his point now that I was no longer a teacher. Both our girls would have liked to have been born into the war machine builders, that part of Fred's family, but they tried to make do with us, blaming me for diluting the bloodline back to the Indian killers who'd settled Fred's ancestral seat.

In May, we had heard that the young men wanted to stay with us for the summer. They were Darlene and Franklin's grandsons, one had dropped out of college twice—bipolar—and the other, a new age Christian studying engineering, was dean's list. By June they were with us twenty-four seven, and it was driving Fred crazy. Crazier. Their stay was a good test, a pre-test for how the apartment on the side of the house would do for Bea when she finally came home or was brought home to us on her shield from California where all girls want to go, she used to say, the good ones and bad ones. And, of course, she did come home, dead, and Cynthia got the apartment, the hand-me-down, she said.

I was stretched thin with all the enabling that was going on, untreated child but grown up daughter of an alcoholic that I am. Fred was sinking into deeper depression as he worked to save the college's endowment as enrollments shrank.

The young men, as they carried out the impossible mission to remodel the long-abandoned home of Fred and Franklin's grandparents—Fred and Franklin are first cousins—were falling apart too, but they had more resources—not money, but reserves of leisure time, and their youth, of course. When they weren't working on the house for Darlene and Franklin who spoke of "the restoration" while Fred spoke of the project as another Iraq or Afghanistan or Syria, they played video games. The house had been stripped and then vandalized. Not much was left of the 1911 house, the one that Franklin had grown up in, and that Darlene had come to as an eight-year-old orphan with her little brother. Even then, she was cheerful and fell for the large, doleful family that she saw as her fate.

Franklin survived D-Day on Omaha Beach, but had seen his brother drown, and Franklin himself was wounded in the heavy surf. He came home wrecked, but Darlene loved him, married him, and they had three sons. She was the driving force behind the old house's renovation. The square house had a row of umbrella trees in the front yard where she had grown up. One of their sons died in his sleep at forty. She wanted the house to be the place where the family, all of us, would have great times.

It was Darlene and Franklin's dead son's son who was the college dropout and who had been in the state mental hospital several times. So, Fred said to Merle, we had a nutcase and an evangelical for the summer who have been assigned to rebuild the Middle East. We had our own project, saving Cynthia, who did not want to be saved. We had our own dead child, our Bea, to grieve.

At eight, Darlene had come with her five-year-old brother, to live in the square house with Franklin's family. She and her little brother had been orphaned, but somehow she grew up, cheerful and pretty, and ready to take on Franklin, ruined from fighting in Europe and Africa. Her little brother grew up, went in the Marines, ran marathons, and had a daughter who became a doctor. They both, brother and sister, were very loyal to all of us in Franklin's family, we never could understand why, but were grateful for Darlene's miraculous cheerfulness and we hoped that we were worth fooling with.

I have known two women of Darlene's appeal, one in her early seventies, one younger in her late fifties. Both were taken care of through terminal illnesses by the husbands they had divorced in order to marry other men. When both second marriages failed—cancer and Parkinson's struck the runaway older brides—they went back to the homes they had raised their children in, back to the men they had left who welcomed them home. I wanted Fred to be like those husbands.

He and Merle had a good laugh about my wish. They said that they did not make husbands that way any longer, and they called my wish my "ask," a word used on TV and sounds, of course, like "my ass."

I would not want to test Fred in that way (leave him for someone else, get cancer, and come home to die), but I have my own test, and so far he is passing it with flying colors—with only a little grade inflation. I asked him to join the Cremation Society with me. This may seem to be a reasonable step for us to take, who had to pay the funeral expenses of our parents. But I saw it as true love, a prepaid fun.

THREE IN ONE

A thousand people came to the funeral of the three people killed on the bridge over the James River at Bremo. A trailer had come unhitched from its tractor and sliced off the top of the SUV whose driver was one of the two doctors at the Health Center. His wife and her ninety-one-year-old mother were with Dr. Neil Walters. He had just taken his mother-in-law to the Center for a checkup, and she needed her daughter, Neil's wife, to go in with her to talk to the other doctor at the Center, their friend, Charles Marion, about her night wanderings.

In his office, Charles had talked to Lena and Marie. He had lost Joey, his only child, twenty-three years ago when he'd gone out on his first solo drive and, speeding, had driven straight into an oak tree just five miles from that bridge at Bremo. Joey Marion's death, like the three on the bridge, was instant. As if that helped. Maybe it does.

Charles spoke at the funeral for his three friends who were buried in one casket. He blamed himself, not the hitch manufacturer, not the driver of the semi who should have checked the hitch. If only Charles had kept Lena and Marie in his office ten more minutes, explaining how to close down a day in a good way to guard against sleep walking or restlessness—no Netflix or ice cream—telling them what they knew as well as he did, but hearing it from him in his office was different from knowing it at home at eleven o'clock and the movie was not over. At home, Neil was just Neil, not a doctor, to his wife and her mother, who loved him but did not listen to him the way they did to Charles, a doctor in his office who had told them that Neil could tell them the very same things. He said in the eulogy that they had laughed when he said they could or should listen to Neil. They said they never listened to Neil, and they liked to hear what Charles had to say.

The huge crowd, so big the funeral was held in the new high school's gym, had laughed. Charles had gone on, blaming himself. If only Charles had taken the time to talk to Neil about the fishing trip to the Outer Banks they had been planning. Charles knew that Neil was waiting for Lena and Marie and was, as Charles knew, planning to surprise them with the proposal that they all go eat Mexican at the new restaurant in Dillwyn. Neil was his good friend all through the university and now with him in this rural outpost treating the new opiate epidemic and the old killers. Ten more minutes of talking about nothing much, and the three of them would be alive. Charles may have been, certainly, he was thinking of his dead son in that same way, but he did not go into the obvious, because he didn't have to. It was almost the same crowd that had been at his son's funeral, also held in the gym, only the old one. If only he had kept Joey at home, refused for some stupid reason to let him drive the car—refused the straight A, soccer team captain Joe.

People had told Charles not to go there, not to beat himself up, that things happened. It was not his fault. It was meant to be. What is, is. Especially death, especially accidents. Period. He must go on. In this case of Neil, Lena, and Marie, there were hidden blessings. One was no nursing home, no physical therapy, no home care, no hospice. Nothing but eternity looming ahead, especially for the ninety-three-year-old Marie, the long-retired math teacher.

Neil had married an African American wife this second time too. Lena. The sons from the first marriage were in medical school as was their mother, one of those older women who went to medical school later and who came to Neil's funeral. Neil was, she explained unnecessarily—one of her faults was explanations—the father of Anthony and Gerald. We all knew the story—best friends, broken marriage. And, she went on unnecessarily, Lena had been her friend, indeed, her best friend. These things happen not just in movies. Lena was, she admitted and we admitted it was true, the better wife for Neil. But no, Lena was not her ex-friend, and never would be an ex anything. It was all very civilized, divorce and race-wise.

Unlike my own family on those two issues, we are Southern in both ways. A divorce for us is Palestine and Israel. Race is a fact that we wish were not bedrock, but it is for us still, unlike it is, or was, for Neil, Lena, and Marie. They were as black as they were white, as white as they were black—ideals. At the funeral many of the mourners came in tee shirts with the photographs of the three on the front and words of comfort on the back like "we will meet at the river, the beautiful, beautiful river," the old hymn filled the gym like waters rising to the rafters. Neil's sons wore white suits, Palm Beach linen, someone said.

They were, we knew, better people than we were. Of course, we voted for Obama and Fred had a cousin go to jail to protest segregated lunch counters in Lynchburg which we thought at the time was silly, having eaten at a lunch counter in Lynchburg. We knew there were real, serious reasons for such protests, but still we were living our lives as if we were above such things.

IT'S HARD TO BE SOUTHERN IF YOU KNOW WHAT IT MEANS

It's hard to be Southern, if that's what you are, and sweet potatoes, ham, and spoon bread are ordinary Sunday dinners. The coleslaw is what you made, chopping the cabbage your brother grew. And one of your best students, an African American football player, says to his classmates, all white, when asked by me, the teacher, what he would point out as a problem with the school, says genially, "Too damn many white people." And your great aunt by marriage says, when asked why she gave away her hydrangea, "It was dying."

But the best example that I know about how hard it is to be Southern is the Jess Meadows one. Here it is:

I knew the truth about what had happened, why May could never "be reconciled" to Jeff Meadows as her young—in their forties—niece and her husband were urging. It was outrageous, but only to May and me, and May could not, would not, say why she couldn't go see Jess Meadows, who was dying and calling Katlin and Howard as well as May's brother in the middle of the night to come sit with him. They were foolish enough to go, stay four hours, and clean out his refrigerator, putting in the soup and bread they had brought with them. Katlin went the first time he called at 2:30 to save her dad from going. She knew he would go and it wasn't right for a man of seventy-five to drive fifteen miles to sit with Jess Meadows until daylight, so she went herself. Typical of Katlin.

After that night with Jeff Meadows—we always called him by his full name as we did all the people we did not like—she and Howard, who can do anything with his hands, took Jess Meadows on as a project, cut his grass, cleaned his house, organized his bills. May was horrified, and one night when she had been told that she should find it in herself to reconcile with Jeff Meadows, she let Katlin and Howard have it, sat them down and told them what had been what. How he had mooched off May's mother, Katlin's grandmother, how he had burned down the old house he'd been pretending to fix up and had been living in, and had, in fact, been born a girl, Jessica Meadows.

It had been forty years ago that the house had burned. It had been set fire to by Jess's current live-in woman. He had been, by arsonist design, in New York, not even in the county, and so had been able to rush back, all distressed. Had come to May's and begged her mother to let him stay with her and May until he could deal with the terrible event. The insurance money built him a new modern house with tall windows that stared down across the low grounds to the river. He had gotten the land, twenty-seven acres, for a song, befriending the old man who had lived there, his son dead in Vietnam. All of that should be enough, May had said, to convince Katlin, if not Howard, that Jess Meadows was a liar, a cheat, a fraud, an arsonist, a transsexual. Not that sex things are ones anyone can choose or help. He was not an artist, though he said he taught art in New York. We had seen his paintings and swore we could do one in about twenty minutes—all one color with droplets as the second coat, but because they were as big as three regular windows, it would take maybe twenty minutes. Ridiculous.

We had met one of his wives, Robin. She was a bird of a woman, now dead with cancer, but then, alive, had been light boned with feathery short hair. First, though, before the cancer, she went crazy. Later, we said it was from living with Jess Meadows who made her give up her two children. Who could make a woman do that? Answer: Jess Meadows.

A WEDDING AND FUNERAL IN VIRGINIA

No one could take it in what Lon Simpkins had done to his wife, Frances. He had broken down and cried at their wedding over twenty years ago, but now he had left her. My brother Ed said Lon had cried because he was smart or had gotten smart at the last minute when it was too late. Any man would have cried when he saw that bride, one of the Parker girls, coming toward him on the path we had made of petals, across the yard of the old house on the river, not a real river, not the James, but the Willis, which is really just a creek. The old Parker house sits up the hill from the Willis, in a stand of oaks. I did not have much room to talk; Fred had wept at his wedding, as he called it. Maybe I should have been the one crying.

Lon was crying, Ed said, because he understood at that moment not just what a crazy woman he had as a bride, but how few acres he was getting, how little he'd have to work with to raise corn on, and how much of an old house he'd have to put running water in and bring electricity to—a twelve room barn of a house. This was long ago in the 1950s before restoring old houses was the thing everyone was doing. But a man's tears at his own wedding?

We took the tears, all of us but Ed, in the best light, that Lon was so in love when he saw Frances Ward Parker walking her nervous little colty walk toward him, all hopeful and lighthearted, trusting that he could fix up her family's place, just the house, since she knew very well that all the farm land had been sold off to Continental Canning Company in the Depression and all she had left was five acres of honeysuckle and some oaks. Of course, Lonnie should have known all this. He could have asked Frances, and the records were at the court house, but he probably thought it would be low minded to check on his bride's property, snoop in the old deed books to see what the property lines really were. He was marrying for love, a family tradition, one that had brought his family "close to ruin." He liked to break into the old hit and spin around singing "Why do fools fall in love/why do they fall in lo-uvh?" He could point to the mystery of it all, how love didn't make sense but who cared anyway. What good did that wisdom do him?

So, later when Lon took off to Utah with the woman who had rented the old trailer from him and Frances, we were as shocked as we had been by the tears at his wedding. Frances had to go to the hospital for a week. At that point, Ed said, the tears Lon had cried at his wedding twenty years ago made more sense. Lon had known at least for that tearful minute at his wedding that he couldn't handle being married to a Parker, especially one of the Ward Parkers, the Valentine Ward Parkers.

Frances's family includes an aunt who took down her Christmas tree knowing that her husband had died in his sleep that night, January fifth. She said she had to get the house ready for all the company that would be coming and since no one knew Winfred had died. She herself had not gone up too close to him or stepped around to the other side of the bed to check on him, but, yes, she had a feeling that he "was gone," so that was why, exactly why, she went ahead with taking the tree down. The needles were dry—it was January and she had put it up without much help from Winfred on December the third—and fell in brown heaps on her grandmother's quilt that she had used to cover up the tree stand.

One of Frances's uncles had let his cattle and pigs inbreed until they were little stunted pygmy herds. He said he couldn't bear to sell them to the abattoirs. That's how he talked and how he thought.

Our favorite Parker story, though, was the one about her second cousin Tavis who killed the wrong person, then bashed the dead man's head in, thinking, we guessed, that so disfigured, the dead man couldn't be identified. He killed the wrong man's girlfriend too, just because she was there watching and screaming. He told the judge "Two wrongs don't make a right," as if that would pass for remorse. We understand that in prison he has converted and leads a prayer group and works in the prison library.

It was a shame that Frances had not inherited that kind of nerve from her Christmas-tree aunt but had gone straight to the hospital when she took in the fact that Lon had really driven away with that woman they had rented the old trailer to. She lacked her cousin Tavis's nerve to go ahead with a plan even if it was wrong. She just stopped living when Lon went off with the woman. When she heard that he had shot himself when he was diagnosed with colon cancer but survived and at the hospital underwent two surgeries, one for the bullet and one for the cancer, it did not give her any relief. In fact, she said it made her feel worse because she wasn't with Lon to nurse him.

I had made the wedding cake for Frances, baked the little dime store ring in the first layer for the children to find, and I had made her dress. Ivory polished cotton with a scoop neck and cap sleeves, tea length, something she could wear a hundred times later in her life if she had led the life we all had seen laid out in front of her.

Lon came home to us to be buried, half of his ashes did anyway. The other half was flung over a creek in Kentucky where he had gone with the woman who had divorced him after he cashed out his life insurance. About fifty people came to the service and the lunch we gave for the family and friends. We all knew most of the story and felt for Frances who acted the part of the grieving widow, which she was in her heart.

After the funeral as I was washing the dishes back in the kitchen, Pauline told me a story I'd forgotten about the day Lon had driven away from Frances who had fixed him a ham sandwich when he came in from mowing the front field. When he had finished the sandwich, he said he was leaving, and left. A few days later, Frances found out where he and the woman were staying, a motel across the river, so she drove there and with the axe she had brought, she broke into their room, but, as she said later, it didn't do any good.

We judged men and women by two standards, one each. The women by their sex lives, and the men by the money they made or didn't make. Frances had ruined her life because she married Lon—her passion for him was crazy, and we never got tired of trying to understand how or why she fell so hard for his boney tilted self in blue jeans. He let her love him for a little while, but he was not worth thinking about because he had lost Frances's farm.

JEHOVAH'S WITNESS

The Jehovah's Witness' name was Maggie. A talker! She had three children in Ohio, two living next door to each other. Could I believe that! And one across Columbus, but it was good, thank the Lord, the way it was, of course, that the brother and sister who had always been so close were living next door to each other! PTL! Maggie was married to Frank for nine years now. His children were in Ohio too, a son who was doing well in Cleveland, and a daughter, well, she had lived there, but she had taken her life. That had happened ten years ago, in fact, the year before Maggie and Frank had married. Maggie was about to become a grandmother again—her daughter was due any day, the one who lived next door to her brother—and Maggie was turning fifty-one this next birthday coming up, also in a few days.

Maggie had a bright, toothy smile, pale blue eyes, and blonde hair swept back in one of those modern messy ponytails that is flipped back up and pinned down on the top of the head so that a plume waves off to the side. This hairdo is one of the many lucky things about young people today, and it worked for Maggie. She had on an old-fashioned trench raincoat, only short, just above her knees, snugly belted around her tiny waist, and big clunky high heels.

We were standing at my front door, all glass, looking out at the van she had driven up in. It was full of friendly Witnesses who waved at us. Maggie dipped her shoulder and waggled her pretty fingers back at them as if she had been gone for some time or was surprised that they were there. Surprise, surprise! It was Frank at the wheel, in coat and tie, and he had the engine running. Maybe that was a planned politeness so that homeowners wouldn't think that the visit would go on for too long, not with an idling van out in the driveway, or maybe it was a getaway strategy in case there were mean dogs growling at Maggie. Frank was in IT for a big, wood products company, and yes, it was sad that so many people had been let go recently, and that made her think of the End of Things or Last Things.

"Did I ever think of what those times would be like?" She opened her Bible expertly to Revelations, which I knew was easy to do—last book—and read some verses to me. "Did I ever think about the dead?" Then she fingered her way back to the front of the New Testament.

All the time, I wanted to say, but was afraid it would sound flippant, so I shook my old head like I had never heard that people died. Which was a lie. I had heard of a person who wished he'd died instead of living with me. That would be my husband of thirty-seven years who was sleeping more and more, sometimes as late as eleven-thirty. In fact, he was still in bed when Maggie drove up. But Maggie seemed too young, even as she was reading from Matthew about what the Kingdom of God really meant to hear about Fred, and I was afraid it would set her off on a series of verses intended to comfort, O comfort "my people."

What would Maggie have said to Andrea if she'd heard her story, the one I'd heard in the Goodwill last Tuesday, how Andrea had been by Nelson's bed in the ICU with him after his heart attack when he got a phone call from his girlfriend. "His what?" Andrea said to me in a dulled, pained way, re-enacting her bedside shock because I'd not been there with her at the hospital and seen it for myself.

"Hi, Baby," Andrea had heard when she picked up the hospital phone, helping Nelson turn toward the phone while flat on his back but still wanting the phone call. The doctor had said let him have what he wanted with a shrug that had meant to Andrea that Nelson didn't have long, that it was all over, but the doctor had meant without knowing he meant it, that it was all over for Andrea who wouldn't understand until four weeks later. It was over for her, for Andrea, the long romance with Nelson, if you could call taking care of his mentally challenged son, Ethan, whose mother had abandoned him legally and Nelson had emotionally, but Andrea, just the girlfriend, had not. When Andrea had understood from hearing the phone call's "Hi Baby," she knew she would have to abandon Ethan too. Andrea said she knew then that she would have to do the same thing to the little guy because she could not nurse a man and take care of his twelve year old with a five year old developmental brain level while his dad was two timing her with this person on the phone whose name she found out was Debbie.

So, the story went on. Andrea had called the court appointed guardian of Ethan and told him her story, and later went to a meeting between the guardian and Nelson, when he had recovered, unaccountably, the doctor said. "It happens." Andrea took the tape recording she had made of another call to Nelson from Debbie—full of "Hey Baby's" and worse. Debbie, it turned out, was married and free only for meeting Nelson at motels, but not free to help out with Ethan. Nelson had lied to the guardian about the stability of his relationship with Andrea in order to reduce his court costs, but then the guardian had picked up his desk phone and called Andrea, asking her if she could come to the office then, right then, to confront Nelson and testify that she was no longer a care giver for Ethan, and to bring the taped conversation with the woman, this Debbie person, the one Andrea had recorded. "It was the hardest thing I have ever done," Andrea said, she, a woman who was twice divorced and once widowed. "Who wants to tell on someone even if that someone deserves it?"

I considered myself an expert on last things, and even after the Jehovah Witness, Maggie, told me about her stepdaughter's suicide in Ohio, I pigeonholed Maggie as an expert only on newer things—second marriage, new grandbabies, up-to-date hair, not last things. She kept cheerfully reading little scriptural tidbits about the end of the world which she said was happening or beginning to happen right now. Then she gave me a book which I tried to pay her for, but she waved at me that girlish wave and dismissed my earthly ways of trying to purchase a treasure beyond all price. She glanced at her watch and we walked out to the vanload of friendly people, and I felt my fingers go up past my shoulder for a little wag. I felt better all day.

What would Maggie have said about Andrea, Nelson, Ethan and Debbie's kettle of fish? My mother used that phrase to cover a great many situations, but mainly ones dealing with my father's regular drunkenness.

THE CHILDREN IN THE WOODS

Just after dark, the children did not come flying out of the woods, not that the adults had missed them or called them. They were all at a party for the man who was retiring, and the kids had to come for various reasons mainly that the babysitters had cancelled. The older ones, twelve and thirteen, were supposed to look after the younger ones, but everyone knows how that works. So when Lucas got himself caught near the top of the sycamore tree not all that far from the river bank, too scared to come down because the branch he was on kept waving, no one knew about it at the house where the wine wasn't exactly flowing but close.

The rest of the children down on the ground tried to help Lucas by yelling up to him, "You can do it," but when they got tired of encouraging him, they tried taunting him and calling him names and threatening that the fire department or the police would come and stretch up the big ladder, maybe two, or get him down in a bucket crane or, they began to hope, with a helicopter, but for that, maybe they'd wait until morning, so he'd better find a way to put his foot down, pointing his toe at the place where a lower limb grew out of the trunk.

It was stupid, on all sides. The parents for letting the kids run out to the woods, assured by the parents of the older boys that they did it all the time, had built a fort etc., etc. It was stupid of Lucas to think that at eight he could impress the older boys. It was stupid of the other guests, all older by different degrees than the parents, and some with grandchildren, not to have stopped the rush to the woods and made enemies for life with the kids and their parents.

"You've forgotten what it's like," the parents laughed nicely. "You should be retiring yourself," is what they meant. It was the newest father who had brought his four-year-old who was weeping quietly while she sucked three fingers. Her dad climbed the tree, and when he got almost to the crown just below Lucas frozen to the tree, he pried him off, feet first down onto his shoulders, and with Lucas' feet wrapped around the newest father's neck, he scraped down the trunk to the ground, taking forty minutes where Lucas' father jerked him back to the house and then into the car, and throwing him into the backseat, and then went back to thank the hostess. No one accepted any responsibility. It was not even a story that would be repeated or remembered.

THE JUDGMENT OF PARIS

The couple was ahead of us, movie star quality, she in platform shoes with hard, tall, polished legs that scissored under her black and white short skirt up the street at a diagonal. Down her back covered in a tiny black jacket was a foot of straight yellow hair. Head down, she slanted up the Charlottesville hill, crossing the street we were slouching along looking for where we'd parked our car. This couple, him all retro preppy-grunge to go home from what party to somewhere in the horsey hills of Albemarle County. If we found our car, we'd go home to our old Victorian half-remodeled pile, in an underwater mortgage. Us, holding out for moving one living daughter back in with us, in the attached apartment. She felt we were a danger to ourselves and to others but has explained that she is not a caretaker.

The young man was a foot taller and not as striking, but in the ballpark. He was all University—khakis, bow tie, sandals, deliberately needing a haircut. Rowing team, I bet myself, seventy-three, on blood pressure tablets, my silent second husband, Fred, sunk into himself but sorry to be that way. "Dissociated," his doctor had explained.

Where do such young people in Charlottesville live? On yachts, moored in a Kubla Khan reservoir five miles beyond the city? On old estates with unraked swimming pools tiled with Italian scenes, not plastic liners? Such a blonde had been murdered the year before after a concert and dropped off in the woods. We had all helped in the search, checking off squares of wooded areas around the old reservoir.

They were heading up Market Street, us tailing them for two blocks. When they passed a line of men sitting on a brick wall drinking out of paper bags, one yelled out, "You are one lucky man. You take care of her. You hear me. Better take care of your own self too!" Approving laughter from the other drinkers cushioned his words, but the young man did put his arm across her shoulder, never slowing down, never glancing over to acknowledge the tribute to his girl. The men looked homeless, but they were still men, whose votes meant everything, admiring and envying the night to come for the young man if he got lucky. We looked at the men and did not think "homeless" or "drunks." We thought "Younger than we are." Age trumps everything, not in a good way.

Fear seized my heart. What would this panel of men say when Fred and I struggled by them, the next couple, us, walking by, not in high, high sandals, my gray hair cut by me, my husband of many years, quieter than usual in spite of his doctor's urging him to talk, to "dis- dissociate." A doctor's joke.

Would they call out to us, "You are one unlucky son of a bitch." Or would an old-fashioned courtesy seal their lips and let us pass by unjudged? Prayer did its trick keeping me focused away from the problem, and I walked on, urging my second husband to catch up, trying not to imitate the regal insouciance, the cool of the old men.

TWO LOVE STORIES

They were both dead now. We were sad about Dab and relieved about Irene who had wrecked as much as she'd had time to and then had thrown in the towel, driving herself to the hospital, not telling Dab where she was headed in the old Porsche that would not go over forty since she had driven it into the big pecan tree in the front yard once to make a point to him about getting off his ass and making some money. Dab got the point but did not have the talent for turning deals his way if they ruined people. He knew better than to go after her in their Ford Escape or call the sheriff who owed him, at least, this. Everyone knew Irene and what she was capable of, both ways—being sweet and being cruel. She kept a pistol in the glove compartment and would sometimes wave it around, but as far as we knew, had never shot at anybody. "Not yet," she liked to yell, and we all knew what she meant.

The river had sandbars and islands. After dinners when there had been drinks—grocery store wine or cheap bourbon—she finished off the whiskey with the melting ice in the glasses and sometimes poured the wine back in a bottle, mixing the pinots and the chardonnays or drank it all. "Willful waste makes woeful want," she'd say as she drank.

Dab had told my brother Ed, his lawyer, that he would go down to the wire to keep his hand in with Irene. She could shoot him, and Ed pointed out that Dab had a scar on his shoulder where Irene had grazed him with her .22. "She wasn't serious," Dab had laughed. "She couldn't miss, even when she was drinking."

This was when Dab had gone to Ed to ask him if Irene had come to Ed's office to start divorce papers, fearing that she might have. Irene was not patient and was known for wrecking good machinery if she got mad enough. A divorce would settle her mind or its alternative.

There was hardly a breeze stirring across the graves at the little church Irene's family had built and had been given the land for, so they ran it as they would have a grocery store. The breeze, the dead, the tombstones, the church all that they stood for or against had no effect, no ameliorating effect on the passionate love/hate Irene had let fester for Dab. He had to leave and death—hers or his—was the best, the simplest, way—land wise. She'd seemed to have given up on the divorce idea, we didn't know why. Then she had gotten sicker.

Ed was at that point on the verge himself of going to the hospital. Fred's and my girls—just Cynthia left now—had been best friends, double bests, double BFFs with Irene and Dab's daughters Zoe, the dancer, and Aster, the barrel racer. Zoe always asked for money for her birthdays and Christmas, with no apologies and Aster, we joked, was short for Disaster, though she was winning in her ways so did not have to ask for money as Zoe had to and resented Aster's freedom from that burden. They were hybrids, of course, from their "crazy parents" they called Irene and Dab.

Dab had run up a lot of debts for those girls— private schools, the right clothes, lessons, camps. You name it. Their mother, Irene, like Dab, wanted the girls to have it all. Why shouldn't they, she'd ask, meaning that she didn't have anything like she deserved. "Always the victim," she learned was her problem though in her case, it was true.

Zoe inherited that view of herself from Irene and was grateful to have a simple way of seeing herself. Aster claimed that she hoped she could do what she'd learned from her mother—be the wrecker who was loved anyway, no matter what.

Take it from him, Fred would imply—if he could live with me, Ed's sister, known for my psychosomatic illnesses, then Dab could make it with Irene. Ed went to see Dab and told him he was a fool to let Irene divorce

79

him. He was using negative hyperbole, he said. Only poor people get divorced, Ed told Dab. The rest of us wait for one or the other to die and then we go on with the money we get left after the funeral expenses and debts. Ed is an unusual attorney as this example shows.

In that conversation, Ed reminded Dab of Brian, his cousin, mine too, of course, by marriage, who had two wives consecutively. We did not like the first wife, Rita, until we met the second, Jana. Then, oh then, as the poet says, we could see how Rita was, in fact, the right one for Brian who was not exactly a prize himself but would do. Brian had a drinking problem. "Who doesn't," he would laugh and offer us one in the morning. Rita would say, "Honey, it's the time of day for coffee, and I have the new pot right here." Brian would kiss her and say, "There you go again," quoting President Reagan to give it some authority.

So Ed finally got Dab to forget his suspicions about Irene's trying to dump him. There was land at stake, and not so much cash. Quite a lot of portable property to deal with. Zoe and Aster would have to divide it all.

Zoe, named for Zoroaster, the Persian star gazer, I think, and Aster, Miss Disaster—she laughed when we called her that. She agreed about land being easier to divide and that was what mattered, Ed said, adding, "To hell with the house and all the stuff. As long as you have the land free and clear." Not what Fred and I could have said then about our Cynthia who would get our mortgage to pay off—on Iraq, as Fred insists on calling our home.

NOT THAT SIMPLE

My brother Ed told me that life got more complicated not simpler. His had. Mine was worse, but I did not bring it up. Ed is younger than I am and does not like to be one-upped on life things.

But here I am: late seventies, and my first love, Hughes Tolliver, is coming back to me. This is the third time he has shown up. The second time hardly counts because that was when Fred was just diagnosed, but we did not know what Stage Four would mean, at least I did not. Brain tumor, and me so sorry for him, and so sorry for me, soon to be all alone. That's when this first love, Mr. Tolliver, who called me his Cougar, which I appreciated so much given the circumstances, appeared. Fred had had it with life. It may have been Bea's death that set his tumor off. Stress and Grief, the twin killers.

NOT JUST THE YOUNG AND
BEAUTIFUL

I was seventy-six when, still working at the college, Fred at home, more or less, that Hughes announced by email that he was and had been in love with me, "for years, actually, forever." This forever spanned the period of my first husband and the retirement and depression of my second and now, the cancer diagnosis.

Hughes was married, more or less, to the mother of two children—not his—both more or less established in their lives, the way modern grown children are, having to hold two jobs each, not able to buy a house, still drinking cheap beer—too much and too often. Depending on the cash flow from Hughes. "Good old Hugely. What would we do without his gifts?" They were grateful and for that, Hughes was grateful he was not their biological father but loved them and was happy to give them money.

"You've got Alzheimer's." I understood what was happening: he wanted to move in with me and my second, dying husband. The guttering candle. Hughes would answer that I still had my wide smile, if not my yellow hair. Not going gently.

"Not yet," I had laughed and yelled, "I am flattered but as our President says, 'You aren't my type.'"

"There's no need to go all shitty on me just because I am telling you the truth. I am offering you some help with what's coming, is on the way, to hit Fred and you."

It was wonderful to feel that he thought he was telling the truth.

THAT'S ONE WAY OF PUTTING IT

"He got the money and I got the debt," Merle compressed her life into an epigram. She could because she had had one semester of Martial. "Who will guard the guards," she often said, especially when it did not seem to me to fit the occasion. Was it just the people in charge who needed investigation?

Still, Merle's raising a random, universal suspicion about the guards did make me think that there were problems with Hughes Tolliver, ones I could not see, that this candidate for the position of palace guard might be dangerous. Hughes Tolliver, the handsome man who had returned after three decades, the high school love of my life, and the man I called Mr. Darcy because he was handsome and looked to me rich and was cleverer than I was. I knew I was mixing up Emma Woodhouse and Mr. Darcy, but why not. Life happens outside books.

Merle told me that I never should have let him come back. The second time. I learned to murmur "That's one way of putting it." Which it was.

When I told her about Hughes's announcement of his lifelong love for me, that I had fallen down, almost, laughing at myself, at my lack of exercise, my gray bushy hair, my 1967 pedal pushers. It was funny, but helpful to me. I swore to Merle that Hughes Tolliver would not ever move in with Fred and me.

Merle is, as you know, my cousin, not Fred's, though she and he feel they are the blood kin, the ones with all the good sense, and I am the interloper from where? Northern Virginia. Fred got his great aunt's big house—which to Merle meant the money, but "who's counting," Fred would smile. He meant that no one in his right mind would ever buy the old place, "Iraq." But land with an old house was almost money, though we had seen several sold for a song or go back to the bank.

It was a Victorian, ten rooms, a long porch that had been tarted up to have colonial columns, but not lived in for over fifty years. Who's counting, Fred had said when we first moved in, being positive in the face of disaster. He got half the farm with the house, the good half of open fields that ran down to the river, not the James, but the Willis that ran into the James a quarter of a mile away. Merle enjoyed saying it was the confluence where Von Steuben had camped, gathering strength to help George Washington. So, the house and half the farm had the weight of history, but no one remembered who Von Steuben was even with the historic sign there. Again, I would say under my breath, "That's one way of putting it."

Our Cynthia used to say when she was speaking to us—we are somehow responsible for Bea's death—that she felt that she was "getting bipolar."

Fred and I took that as one of Cyn's bleak, dark, funny as hell lines, "getting bipolar." Like Merle's. But later in the long deep silence, we thought maybe she was right. She had been to a shrink who had diagnosed her, and she was letting us know, slowly, letting us down slowly with a joke.

AT ONE OF THE PARTIES

I felt stupid that it hurt my feelings. The poem Fred had written about my dancing with Hughes, when he'd shown up out of the blue at one of the parties at the courthouse. The poem turned out to be not about me, my dancing or jealousy. I had been sure for years that the poem meant that Fred was jealous when he had seen me dancing with Hughes, stared at me through the darkening window "spinning like a top" with Hughes's hand on my waist, laughing and happy. "No," Fred said when asked by a friend what the poem was about, "it was not about jealousy, not anything to do with the lavender dress swirling around knees. In fact, as far as I knew, Florence did not have a lavender dress. She hated the color, 'an old woman color.'" This is what Fred said I had said about lavender. "No," Fred went on mildly, "the poem is about death, and what it is like—being outside the party, the music, the dancing— all of that, nothing personal, just about me being on the wrong side of the window."

And, worse, I felt guilty for putting my feelings above what Fred was now facing and what had happened to our neighbor whose daughter had been kidnapped and probably killed, thrown in one of the

ponds where Fred went fishing. Where Martin
Hillander had drowned.

CAMELLIAS IN THE SNOW

The December weekend I thought Hughes, the man I called Mr. Darcy until I called him Wickham, the bad guy in *Pride and Prejudice,* and I were driving to Charleston to pretend we were getting married in one of the old churches in that beautiful slave-market city, was the weekend he told me that he was going back to his wife, who was not, it became clear, the ex at all, the drinker whose vomit he had cleaned up and who had refused to let his grown children from his first marriage visit him in their five bedroom house. Let me hasten to remind myself that the three of us—I and Hughes, and my husband Fred, left in the care of Home Hospice, are all close to eighty. Fred in one of his clear moments had urged me to go to Charleston for the weekend with Hughes. It may sound terrible but wait until you get there, the big threshold before you judge.

Hughes calls it Episcopal Adultery or No Harm No Foul. He and I are both, in fact, very much married to others, but we feel that we ourselves may as well be married. We did not mean for this to happen. No, Fred is the better man by far, but he is dying. Hughes used to leave and come back, but now he says he is back for good. He doesn't ask if he can stay, he just stays. But, typical of him, he is telling me he will be returning to his wife.

The ex-wife, or wife-still, is the woman Hughes has been married to for nine years, then she tried to divorce him, but I am not sure it went through. Then, he staged the reunion with me, the woman he said every day was saving his life. Me. Every day.

So how did it make sense that Hughes would take me to Charleston to tell me he was going back to his ex-wife? The woman who took him off their checking account, but kept herself on his health insurance, and who would not, as I said, let his children visit him at their home.

I did not think Hughes would have been able to explain it so I could pretend to believe it. One of my explanations for his lies and betrayal is that dementia has hit him, though it seems to me that it swoops in conveniently. Most of the time, hearing about his latest badness, I thought that he did not want to explain anything. He was not demented, just a con man. He just left when it suited him. Before he closed my front door, he'd said, so sincerely, "Merry Christmas." Just the way a person would say it, who was normal, who had not lost touch with what's what. Who could say such a thing after breaking someone's heart? But he knew that with Fred dying I had plenty to keep me occupied. He actually thought that.

When I said back, with knives in my voice, "And a merry Christmas to you too, Hughes," he seemed to think I meant it, and that things were ending nicely after their six month interlude of happiness, the three of us making a little life together in "Iraq." Hughes appreciates Fred's calling our half-renovated house Iraq, a war zone, which it is, a ruined landscape, in several ways. Maybe he thought that he had brought me happiness—which he had—if only it had not been floating on lies, just bobbing along.

How could he think that he was being wished a merry anything, leaving as he did? My doctor said he was stupid—that was his diagnosis. I said he was crazy, and my husband of many years, my second, Fred, said in another clear moment that Hughes needed treatment, thinking of his own case, very different, but the same in a general sense.

Hughes's ex-wife or still-wife had stopped drinking, or said that she had, and he was going back. It had been six months—his living with me and Fred, and his divorce papers had come through, or he said they had. Six months since the week after the funeral of my sister, Lena.

Hughes had read about Lena's death in the paper and had come to her funeral knowing that I would be there of course. He had seen me at our school reunion, the fiftieth, the first time we had seen each other since that time three years earlier in the antique shop in Alta Vista when I had driven Cynthia there to find the crystal doorknobs that she wanted to sell online. When the minister had asked if anyone else would like to speak about Lena, Hughes had walked up to the front of the crowded church and told stories about our childhoods, his, mine, and Lena's—catching minnows in the creek, eating the squirrel stew that Lena had made from the ones he brought back from hunting. His own mother would never do this and had slapped him across the kitchen for dripping squirrel blood on her floor.

It was clear at Lena's funeral that Hughes was recalling how he had loved me and my family since he and I were in the seventh grade. The fact that he told such stories about Lena renewed, not that it needed renewing, my buried love for him after almost half a century and my two marriages—one still legal in Iraq.

I have come to think of his showing up at Lena's funeral as Hughes's stalking me, then a few weeks later, driving up in my yard, parking his truck and saying that he would live there in his truck, but after a few cold nights, moving in with me, invited into the half re-done house. It was mid-October by then.

He knew me well enough from our high school romance to know that I would not stand for anyone I loved to be out in the cold, me, whose daddy tamed squirrels, never killed them. He knew, must have, that if he parked in my driveway, it would not be long before he was in my house, and when he got in, he would begin cooking and cleaning just like the ideal husband. But the real and present and dying husband, Fred, was there. Fred. The man who awakened from a deep sleep when I shook him to say that the house painter named Clarence had driven up and was putting up his ladder, said not opening his eyes but emphasizing certain words: "*Clarence* is *come*, false, fleeting perjur'd *Clarence*. That stabb'd me in the field by *Tewkesbury*. Seize on *him*, furies, take *him* to your torments!"

Even I, who am very "limited," as my grandmother often said, could not forsake this dying husband who quoted Shakespeare almost asleep, dying, for my first love who killed squirrels and drove a pickup, who left me saying "Merry Christmas" sincerely.

It must have been a shock for him too at Christmas—to leave me. He had been very happy with me (and Fred), hanging the last of the sheetrock in our basement, going out to dinners or having them ready for me when I came home and keeping Fred company. We took weekend trips, twice to Charleston and to small towns in the Blue Ridge. I brought back small jars of relish, jellies, and homemade soaps from these jaunts, as I called them, and once a whole cake, famous in Piedmont, Virginia, the hot milk cake. It melted in my mouth and in Fred's. Our Bea made us happier than happy when she was a baby, but after that sadder than sad, and then she died on an icy road. That's an old story we have had to live with.

Hughes's presence made me happy, happier than I thought possible with Fred dying and Bea dead. We never watched television, just talked about our pasts, how we had missed our chance to have a good life together, having children with each other instead of with the wrong man and woman—not that Fred was wrong, just unexpected because Hughes had been the expected one.

That may have been what was wrong, for our happiness to have come so late, or at all. It is hard for a person whose husband is dying to know any level of happiness. The way it gives lightness to ordinary things, even if it flickers on and off. Still, Hughes must have loved those times with me and Fred. He told me that he could not see how anyone could have been mean to me when he heard about my first husband—damaged goods, who expected me to clean up all his money problems, and who put his fist through the wall in the bedroom, a hole next to the bed. I had kept the first husband's violence, what is now called domestic abuse, a secret from Bea and Cynthia who would ask why I was divorced before I married their dad. When I had tried to tell my mother about how unhappy I was, I was told that all married women are. My mother had stood everything except a bad husband, and she left my brother and me thousands of dollars she kept under her mattress so the government wouldn't take any. One of her virtues was a loyalty that went too far.

Hughes had been practicing with my church choir for a solo part in the Christmas service, and it was assumed—maybe by him too—that he would be singing as a married man—a bigamist, I thought in retrospect. But then, having come back from the trip to Charleston, married at last to me, the girl, now an old lady, the girl he'd left at seventeen to join the army because he had been told that I was riding around with Walter Anderson. I had not been.

As I say, we are old, not the time of life when the dark roots of romance are exposed, we thought, but the time of life when things go better, when camellias bloom in the winter, often in the snow, the time when we would get into the getalong as my dead aunt called it. Even for us, who had taken care of very old parents, very ill ones, old age seemed to be a faraway place where there was a kindness even if it was one mixed with indifference, but still, a deep and reliable kindness.

Wrong again.

CAMPING AT THE SOUTH POLE

Cynthia, our older daughter and our only daughter after her sister Bea was killed in the wreck, called us late one night two weeks after the baby was born. Could we come help her with things while she finished up the project for her company? She was lucky to have the job because she could work at home and Chase, her "partner" had never had a job. He was an artist on computers. So, of course, Fred and I packed up the Focus and were off like a shot the next morning for the ten-hour drive. When we walked in that evening, Chase did not turn around from the kitchen sink where he was eating a peach, the juice dribbling down. We kept standing in the kitchen door expecting him to turn his head at least, or to say with his mouthful of a Georgia Belle, "Glad you folks are here. The baby's great."

But he never turned his head, never said anything. Their kitchen was so small, and we are both large—always starting diets—so with the three of us, it was tight. Cynthia was there in the next room with the baby who was making little baby grindings, like a toy. So we stood there and answered the questions that had not been asked. "We had a good trip, stopped twice, once in

Charlotte. Traffic wasn't too bad, and the rain didn't really start until a little bit ago."

Nothing. So, we trundled backwards past Cynthia and the baby, Miranda Walker, named after two of Chase's aunts, into the small living room, then started unloading the car in the almost dark. By then it was almost nine. We found the guest room, a funny name for a room with a bed with no sheets or lamps, just a weak overhead bulb, but we put all our stuff there in a corner, not hanging up anything because the closet was overflowing. Then I took the cooler bag into the kitchen where Chase had finished his peach and had gone into his and Cynthia's room and shut the door. I took out the things I'd brought from our freezer at home, stocked from Sam's Club over the past month, hoping that we'd be asked to come help with the baby.

This cold shouldering went on for six days. On the seventh day, not like God who rested, but exhausted from having to use the bathroom but not knowing where the towels were kept or toilet paper, from having to eat secretly—sandwiches from the chicken we'd brought, and I'd Crockpotted on the third day—we said we thought we'd go home the next day. Then, like speeded up global warming, Chase made us feel welcomed, talked to, laughed with, and we, so desperately relieved, so happy, instantly got over our camping experience on the frozen ice plains of their tiny house, mortgaged to the hilt. But the next morning as we were leaving, Cynthia rose up from her computer to kiss Baby Miranda in my arms and asked if we could stay two more nights because her boss had added an extra component to her assignment. We said, of course, we could. We refused to admit that the one day when we were expected to leave was sunny; when we said "of course, we would stay," the icy skies fell again from Chase. It was as clear as an email in all caps: I DO NOT WANT YOU HERE. It was also clear that Cynthia had all she could deal with, so we did not give any sign that anything was wrong, that our body temperatures were at dangerously low levels, that there was no feeling in our extremities.

Jesus would point out that Chase had been and still was out of work and that his own mother had just been there to help out for two weeks. She was very close to the baby, Chase said, calls her Mir, which sometimes sounds like Miracle. He would tell Cynthia so we could hear, that his mom held the bottle higher so Mir did not get bubbles. Two more days of severe blizzard set in. Then, the morning we packed up to leave again, the sun came out.

Fred said that it's a good thing that the Stockholm Syndrome exists. He means that we accommodated ourselves to the conditions in the little house. He understands this way abused people act from his therapist. It took a week plus the two extra days—beginning that first night with Chase in the kitchen eating the peach and ending a century later with our pulling out of their driveway—for us to adjust to life at the Pole, but we did. We never even looked at each other to commiserate or lift an eyebrow, and we never slept in the same bed because I slept on a futon in Baby Mir's room so Cynthia and Chase could get some rest. Fred couldn't sleep in the bed that had a thin foam and rubber pad for the mattress. The dog that had been treated like their first child was locked out and ran around the house all night scratching at the little windows and doors, whimpering and whining.

We did not feel sure that we could go back. Could survive. Once, we did swear we would stay in a Super 8 or Microtel if we ever got asked back. But we didn't mean it, and we haven't been asked back, even when Baby Mir went to the emergency room with an allergic reaction to her new formula. We are in denial about our camping at the South Pole and grateful to be.

Fred heard a story on the radio about a dyslexic boy who finally at eleven learned to read by imagining himself to be a boy who could read. This power has helped us immensely: we imagine that we are happy, and bingo, we are. We are trying it retroactively by seeing our visit as a good visit, and we are waiting for the bingo. We are trying to imagine Cyn and Mir living in the attached apartment. Chase can visit, and his mom.

SEVENTY-FIVE MILES PER HOUR

I knew that Hughes was driving too fast, and in a hard rain. As we passed the Escalade, I saw the driver waving so I waved back and so did Hughes.

Why did I not tell him to turn around, take me home where he has been living this second time for six months when I helped him live through his stepson's death, gave him a sanctuary, rescued him. He was a "refugee" he said. And, I myself needed help with Fred, home alone tonight with his cancer.

I needed the steak dinner at Raleigh's Steak House over in Woodland. I am making fun of my deadly situation, with my real, legal, dying husband at home while I am hurtling toward eternity just for a steak dinner with the man I have also loved with interruptions since we were in high school, this man driving drunk in the rain at 75 mph.

Now, I hope we will be killed, but who will take care of Fred? I have a cousin who puts flowers, real ones, not plastic, on her ex-husband's grave, the husband she left for an old boyfriend. We still say boyfriend. The word means liar.

Did I sell my soul for a nice evening? I don't drink, so it was a 1953 evening when most women did not drink, even adulterers, like me. I did not know Hughes drank, but he was acting drunk. We are old—he is seventy-nine, and I, once a cheerleader, am a little behind him, but old enough to know better, not to be re-enacting our teenage romance when he thought I had given him up and so joined the army. I got married, once, then twice, had two daughters—one is dead.

Hughes's story is similar: married, children, divorced, and then again with stepsons. But this time, it was the wife, Joanna, who drank, as we used to say about alcoholics. He would wipe up her vomit and take her to dry out. This was the woman in the Escalade who would be dying with Hughes and me.

Was she rich? Richer than I was. Beautiful? About the same level as me, though my taste in clothes and, I'd bet, in furniture—all family pieces, and rugs, all oriental—is much better. What is it about her, this dragon woman who would not allow Hughes's sons to visit him in their home, the one he added a room to, the one he'd installed solar panels, the one he paid for a new roof?

I cannot answer my own questions even with Jesus's not taking the wheel to save us for the steak dinner which I now think—off and on—was his attempt at a farewell dinner.

You had to be there to feel his appeal. He thinks he has sex appeal, and maybe that is what it is, but there is also the appeal of the past and how it still operates, sending out dangerous shadows that cover up the pain.

The first time he left? No steak dinner, just silence, just not there when I came home that afternoon.

IMPROVEMENT

My story goes on in my head. This time Hughes's leaving is different. An improvement—the steak dinner and the drag race with his ex-wife. There is a kind of ceremony to it, a kind of celebration in the way, that for some people, a funeral is a celebration. Going to a better place, released from suffering, crossing the river, finding peace. What it will be soon for Fred.

But the night is young and when we get to Raleigh's and I am thinking that at least, I would soon be eating my sirloin, medium rare, and putting sour cream on my baked potato and blue cheese on my salad, that the worst is over. We are alive, not arrested. We will go on, one way or another. Then I hear "Hey, Hughes! I beat you, didn't I?"

And, Hughes? He does not miss a beat, says "I knew you would. Joanna, this is Florence, who has taken me in after you kicked me out."

I am stunned. Sick at heart, but still stupid, blind as a bat. If she had asked us to come sit with her and her friends or whoever they were, surely Hughes would have refused.

Guess what. We go over to her table, sit down, and I meet her two daughters, Tanya and Sandra, and order.

For me, the most expensive and biggest steak and a dessert—the pecan pie with ice cream. Hughes, low in cash as usual, is nudging my foot which means, slip me that hundred dollar bill in your wallet, but I cross my legs and do not receive the nudge and hear him order the hamburger. Joanna orders a Caesar salad and laughs, alone, that she is watching her figure. Tanya and Sandra go to the salad bar and load up, looking bored to death with this evening.

Joanna wastes no time and fixes her big blue, mascaraed eyes on me. "How long do you think this old playboy will be with you this time?"

And I, for once in my life, can think of the right answer. "Just a few hours. Long enough for him to get his stuff. Some time tonight he'll be gone."

In this killer exchange as my mood brightens and Tanya and Sandra return, I cut my big brown eyes, often praised for being bullets, deadly, over to Hughes who had told me before we began the drive at dark that he loved me and yearned for me when I left in the mornings for work. I think, or thought, he meant it. He often would tell me without one drop of irony what a good husband and father he had been, and that he wanted to be my next husband. He was sincere. I will stand by that until my cremation.

It is hard to love a crazy man. I tried and know that I am to blame to some degree. Who wouldn't love the house vacuumed twice a week, blueberry muffins made from scratch with coffee from roasted and freshly ground beans?

Where on earth is such a woman? Not at my house, I hope. I would kick her out along with Hughes.

THE NEXT MORNING

After the evening in hell for the steak dinner, after watching Hughes load his truck with his things—the nice shirts I'd given him still in their LL Bean papers, his duffel bag, his computer—I slept like a baby, not that my babies ever slept through the night, but I was exhausted from what I'd been through at Raleigh's, meeting face to face the Joanna I had heard so much about and not only her, but those two daughters who stood at the salad bar laughing at something.

The next morning, the truck is still in my driveway. Frost is on the windshield. I step out and up to the window and there Hughes is, sound asleep, bent like a knife, but asleep in his coat (my gift from Orvis). I tap on the window and he sits up, a smile on his handsome face. "I thought you would not let me freeze to death."

"I almost did. I wish I had."

"Let's go in and have some of your good coffee, the best in the world."

"Just for coffee"

"Yes. I need to explain last night. I set it all up to make you jealous, I hoped. Remember that you are the one who did this first to me. Started going around with Walter Anderson when you were, I thought, helping your sister with those twins of hers."

"I was helping, and you know it. Those twins were and are killers, and I had to watch them and tie them down with ropes or they'd be dead. I did not have time to be going around with anybody. I was in a coma every night."

"Whatever. I thought you were seeing him and leaving me high and dry so I joined up and when I got home in two years, you had a house and a husband—not this one, Fred. Joanna may be a little bit alcoholic, but she is smart and was willing to try to offload me to you, to play act the part, have some fun, make you jealous and make you think seriously about marrying me."

"It made me think seriously about a murder, a double murder."

"I could see that."

By then he was back in my kitchen where he'd been for six months. He knew where his coffee mug was, where his pint of half-n-half was in the refrigerator, and, I would find out, where he had hidden his toothbrush.

In a few minutes he was explaining what a good person I was and how I had saved his life. He knew that

I knew better than anyone how mean and angry his mother had been to him, how bullied he'd been in the second grade, so bad that he'd sneak into the woods and stay there all day until the school bus came by in the afternoon and he could pretend he'd been in school. About his dead stepson.

That's how he returned for the third time, but I am ready for the next departure.

ROBBING BANKS

I know it's wrong to be thankful that our children, I mean the one we still have, did not do what other people's have, but I am. Here's an example.

We drove into the yard still upset from our visit to the shrink who had issued a summons, all nicely coated with the slime of being helpful, for me to come in for a session for which I would be charged only half price, because why? I needed some help with how to talk to Fred. Naturally, I refused, furious at the finger pointing at me for the post-suicide-attempt problems.

Anyway, we drove into our second-mortgaged yard, and there we saw the Yukon of our old friends, the Prichards. Friendliest people in the world. They have six grandchildren, all of their children happily married and holding down jobs. They had driven out from the city to surprise us and, not finding us at home, never suspected that we were at a shrinks. They had made themselves at home, dug up some Queen Anne's Lace to take home for their borders, and were sitting on our patio, drinking ice water—we never lock our doors—when we drove in, me still mad as fire, Fred, sadder than usual, trying to make everything right which can never happen even after we are dead. I tell him all the time that when I see him at the gates of hell, he will understand what he did to me. He always says he is sure he will and that will be the good thing about being dead, that he can at last make it up to me by getting it straight. You can see why I loved him for saying that, and why he let my first love, Hughes, move in with us after the doctor, a real one, not the shrink, said the cancer was stage four. Six months at the most.

As I said, we never lock our doors. Why bother? Out in the country where we tried to renovate the old 1870s house? The thieves would just break the windows, slit the screens, look around at our appliances, 2003 computers and big heavy TV's, and leave.

The Pritchards, Grant and Ellen, were sitting there, waiting for us to show up, and when we did, we had a good time, in fact, got over our fight which I had to do the heavy lifting in. What they told us, laughing a little, rueful, was that their niece was in the women's correctional facility near us, and that they had waved at it as they drove by on the way out to see us. What had she done?

We didn't know any children in jail. I don't count my students who go for DUIs and drug deals made to undercover DEAs, informing on their friends. Their visit was better than any therapy could be. For me, anyway.

Their niece with the lovely name of Emilia Grace, mother of two biracial babies, one autistic, kept by Emilia Grace's long suffering mother, the sister of Grant, had lost her job as an aide at the veterans' hospital, so on a Tuesday morning last February, she had walked into the biggest bank downtown, First Federal, stuck her pointed finger through her big sweater's pocket, and asked for all the money in the teller's drawer. She was shocked that the woman handed over the money and even put it neatly in the shopping bag for her as if it were groceries.

Here Grant laughed sadly and asked for another glass of water. Then, he went on, Emilia Grace had walked out of the bank with her bag full of money, gone to a coffee shop, ordered a large coffee and crumb cake, called her mom to tell her what she had just done and that she was sorry. Her mom had called Grant at work, and he got Ellen to go over to watch the two babies while he went to his sister's, picked her up, and drove her downtown to get Emilia Grace who had finished the crumb cake by then and was weeping. They drove Emilia Grace back home, left the bag of money with Ellen and the babies, and then the three of them went to the police station. That's how Ellen and Grant have a niece in jail and that's why I am grateful and thrilled when I think of Fred's and my Cynthia and our dead Bea, who I think is in a cloud, a cirrus one. Even with

Bea dead, who never robbed a bank, I know she might not have regretted it immediately, and neither she nor Cynthia certainly would have called us.

Since that visit, we know that Grant has had to go to another prison to visit Emilia Grace who has now a third baby delivered while she was in prison that Social Services has placed twice. Grant and Ellen shook their heads. We did too. Grant laughed his sad laugh.

They promise to visit us again, the us being Fred and me and Hughes, in the old half-renovated house and say they can see why Fred calls it Iraq. They do not lift an eyebrow when I said that an old friend has been staying with us, off and on. "My old boyfriend."

They understand robbing banks and an inappropriate visitor, as my mother would call Hughes.

NO AND YES

Wesley had not seemed angry because Aline had said no, she was not interested in lying down on her bed with him and watching television, so he had said in his matter of fact way that he'd be pushing off. It was almost dark and night driving was getting harder. He had postponed his cataract surgery, what his friends, the ones who were still around that had been so kind when Mary died, had told him about: go in to the doctor, come home, and the next day he'd be reading the paper without glasses. Then Wesley, standing by her door, invited her to come to his wedding. Aline said yes and went to the wedding the next month. The bride hugged her and thanked her for being so kind to Wesley.

ABOUT THE AUTHOR

Susan Pepper Robbins lives in rural Virginia where she grew up. Her first novel was published when she was fifty ("One Way Home," Random House, 1993). Her fiction has won prizes (the Deep South Prize, the Virginia Prize) and has been published in journals. Her collection of stories "Nothing But The Weather" was published by the small press Unsolicited Press, and her second novel, "There Is Nothing Strange," was published in England in 2016 by Holland House Books. Another novel, "Local Speed," came out from Unsolicited Press. and a new collection of stories "The Turn Key Job and Other Stories" is coming out in 2021. Her stories focus on the drama of ordinary lives in the "new" South. She teaches writing at Hampden-Sydney College and wrote a dissertation on Jane Austen at the University of Virginia.

ABOUT THE PRESS

Unsolicited Press is a small press in Portland, Oregon. The progressive publishing house was founded in 2012 by editors who desired a stronger connection with writers. The team publishes award-winning fiction, poetry, and creative nonfiction.

Learn more at www.unsolicitedpress.com.

CPSIA information can be obtained
at www.ICGtesting.com
Printed in the USA
BVHW031923281121
622722BV00006B/495